MORE THAN A WOODLOT

Getting the Most from Your Family Forest

Stephen Long

with
Virginia Barlow
Irwin Post
Michael Snyder
Charles Thompson
Chuck Wooster

A Northern Woodlands Book

PUBLISHED BY

Northern Woodlands
PO Box 471 | 1776 Center Road
Corinth, Vermont 05039-0471

802-439-6292 | www.northernwoodlands.org

All photographs by the author unless otherwise noted.

Illustrations by Joe Smith
Book design by Jenna Dixon : djinna.com
Proofread by Rachael Cohen : rachaelcohenwordwright.com
Indexed by Jan Williams : janwilliamsindexing.com

Library of Congress Control Number: 2012931544

5   4   3   2   12   13   14   15   16

ISBN 978-0-9786599-4-3

Printed and bound in the United States of America.

Printed with vegetable oil-based ink on acid-free and elemental chorine-free paper containing 30% recycled post-consumer waste, certified by the Sustainable Forestry Initiative.

A book worth the tree.

MORE THAN A WOODLOT

To my four grandchildren –
Aidan, Cecilia, Lucca, and William –
and to all of those who are just
learning to love the woods

CONTENTS

INTRODUCTION

This book is written for woodland owners who would like to learn more about their forest, manage it with sensitivity, and leave it in a better condition than they found it. Gone are the days when most people viewed their forest simply as their private source of fuel, fence posts, and lumber. Today's owners of family forests have different needs and goals for their woodlands.

Managing woods can mean imposing your will on a natural system, or it can mean working with the natural system to enhance what it can offer you and future owners. There is a chasm of difference between the two, and I am a firm believer in the latter approach. If you take the time and develop the skills to understand what you have to work with, you can engage in management that works with—rather than against—natural processes. By understanding forests as dynamic systems, you can see how best to participate in that dynamism.

Forests are natural systems that contain resources that have commercial value. There are ways to capture some of that value while not degrading the forest's other noncommercial values. When

people don't understand the implications of their management decisions, it's easy to both reduce the value of a forest and put its well-being at risk.

The world has changed dramatically in the last couple of decades. That holds true in almost any realm you name, including forestry. As it's practiced in the forests of the Northeast—which we define as New England and New York—forestry has undergone a significant transformation.

Public concerns about forests and forest management have sparked much of the change. Societal distaste for clearcutting has led to timber harvesting regulations in several states. In tandem with other concerns, it also gave rise to forest certification programs, which award a green seal of approval to an enrolled owner of a forest that passes periodic audits of its management practices. Many corporate owners have adapted their procedures where necessary to meet the strict environmental and social standards of the certification programs because the seal of approval gives them access to certain markets.

The way that forestry is practiced in the millions of family forests has also evolved. Systems and methods that work well in a large corporate or government holding—including those that pass muster in the certification systems—are not so easily transferred to the scale of the family forest, which is measured in acres, not square miles.

Simultaneously, wider recognition of timber harvesting as an acceptable land use has emerged within the mainstream environmental organizations. More and more people have come to recognize the important role of the forest products sector in employing local workers and paying local landowners for their wood. Timber harvesting provides a measure of stability in the land base and serves as the best hedge against the suburbanization of the woods. A forest that remains a forest is in the best interests of any environmentalist.

As its subtitle suggests, this book is designed to help you get the most out of your family forest. It begins with some context for your land, both historical and ecological. It then provides information on management plans, working with a forester, principles of silviculture, timber harvests, reporting income from timber sales, and ways to prepare for the eventual transfer of ownership to an heir. It should provide any owner of a family forest the means to take an active and enjoyable role in the future of that forest.

I am not a forester, but I've been covering this subject as a journalist for 20 years. For longer than that, I've owned a 95-acre family forest in Vermont, which has been my learning laboratory. All along, I've had a forester managing our forest, and I've absorbed as much as I possibly can from that professional advice. So I bring the perspective of a family forest owner and a journalist to this book. I also bring the backup of a number of experts.

This book has six co-authors. We began with a structure for the book, assigned chapters, and each of the writers produced his or her work. I am one of the six, and besides writing my own chapters, my role has been to edit the others so that we spoke with one voice and formed a seamless whole. The co-authors have contributed their own original work to this effort, and their grasp of the subject and their perspectives on forestry and land ownership have helped to enrich it. The success of this book owes a great deal to co-authors Virginia Barlow, Irwin Post, Michael Snyder, Charlie Thompson, and Chuck Wooster.

Together, we hope to inspire thousands of landowners to become engaged in the management of their forests and foster in them an abiding sense of stewardship.

—*Stephen Long*

CHAPTER 1

OUR 21ST CENTURY FOREST

Measured in photographs per mile, it would be hard to beat the Northeast's woodlands in late September and early October.

Autumn invites people to flock here from around the world to take in the colors otherwise not readily seen in nature: gold, scarlet, yellow, orange, even purple. The changing of the maple, ash, beech, and aspen amazes all of us—visitors and natives—each year.

In other seasons, the forest can seem like little more than a backdrop to a picture; in fall, it has an opportunity to play the starring role. Visitors driving along state or town highways and even the interstates could easily assume that all those beautiful hillsides are part of a national forest or state park, but that's rarely the case in the Northeast.

Here, the vast majority of the land is privately owned. From state to state, there are differences in the ratio of private to public ownership of forestland, but even New York, which has two large state-owned forest preserves, the Adirondack Park and Catskill Park, is 63 percent privately owned. The New England states combined are 92.6 percent private.

This public-private ratio differs greatly from that of the western states, where, for example, private landowners own just 10.8 percent of Alaska and 29.6 percent of Utah. This distinction between private and public land is important because most of the region's wood products are harvested from privately owned forests.

But public forests continue to serve many purposes, too. Like all forests, they provide an amazing array of what have come to be known as ecosystem services. They filter water, purify it, and reduce the chance of floods. Trees absorb carbon dioxide through their leaves and store it everywhere from roots to crown. Forests are home to a complex web of interacting plants and animals, predators and prey. And forests provide recreational opportunities year-round, with the White Mountain National Forest being one of the most highly used national forests in the nation. More than six million people visited it in 2010, a greater number than visited some of the popular national parks. Clearly, these public forests serve the public good.

So do the private forests. Over the years, with increased understanding of how to

State	Land area	Percent forested	Public ownership acres	Private ownership acres
Connecticut	3,500,000	51.3	411,000	1,383,000
Maine	19,300,000	91.6	1,098,000	16,575,000
Massachusetts	4,900,000	64.7	992,000	2,179,000
New Hampshire	5,700,000	85.1	1,204,000	3,646,000
New York	30,200,000	61.8	4,231,000	14,438,000
Rhode Island	640,000	55.6	53,000	303,000
Vermont	5,900,000	78.3	754,000	3,864,000
Total	70,140,000	72.9	8,743,000	42,388,000

Figure 1.1 Private and public ownership of land in New York and New England.
Data compiled from Brett J. Butler, *Family Forest Owners of the United States*, U.S. Department of Agriculture Forest Service, Northern Research Station, 2006.

keep forest systems healthy and productive, foresters have worked with private landowners to ensure that forests still provide these ecosystem services while continuing to provide wood for a wide variety of products. That means that the daily decisions about the future of this landscape are in the hands of the millions of people—and perhaps you're one of them—who own a bit of that forest.

That choice of the word "forest" ending the preceding sentence is made deliberately because many people think of rural land in the Northeast as largely agricultural. It's true that farmers continue to work the land, particularly where soils and topography make it possible to do so profitably, and there has been a rebirth in agriculture based largely on an increasing interest in eating food grown closer to home. Still, the Northeast—which we'll define throughout this book as New England and New York—began losing ground as a center of agriculture around the time of the Civil War. Today, 73 percent of the land in the Northeast is forested. People who own land are most likely to own forests.

We are enveloped by forests. The question of what will become of them is at the heart of this book. The region has a long history of stewardship but also a long history of exploitation. The direction we take depends on the actions of those millions of landowners. And yes, it is millions. (See the table in Figure 1.1 that shows ownership of land.) Will they take good care of the land, or will they see it as a resource whose sole purpose is to be exploited? Deeper still, will they know the difference? It is our hope that this book will provide forestland owners with the tools and the knowledge to make thoughtful decisions about their use of the land. If they do, this magnificent forest will continue to thrive and provide sustenance to the plants, animals, and people who depend on it and call it home.

State	Owners of 1–9 acres	Owners of >9 acres	Average size of holding	Family acres	Other private/ non-family acres
Connecticut	88,000	13,000	14	898,000	485,000
Maine	148,000	85,000	71	5,727,000	10,848,000
Massachusetts	261,000	29,000	8	1,686,000	493,000
New Hampshire	81,000	43,000	29	2,358,000	1,288,000
New York	382,000	232,000	24	11,252,000	3,186,000
Rhode Island	34,000	3,000	8	204,000	99,000
Vermont	46,000	41,000	44	3,109,000	755,000
Total	1,040,000	446,000	29	25,234,000	17,154,000

FOREST HISTORY

Before the coming of the European settlers beginning in the seventeenth century, this land had long been home to many nations of native peoples. The arrival of Europeans was a death knell to many of these nations, whose populations were decimated by smallpox and scattered by empire building. When Europeans arrived, they found forest covering an estimated 96 percent of this landscape, with interruptions in it primarily in the broad river valleys, where Indians periodically cleared bottomland by burning it and growing crops in the rich soil. (I use the word Indian, because most Native Americans use the term themselves and prefer it.)

What were those original forests like? With a dearth of clues, it's hard to be certain. A few patches of old-growth forest have lasted to this day, but forest ecologists point out that it's a mistake to draw general conclusions from these particular remnants because they were an anomaly even at the time of settlement. They re-

mained uncut for a number of reasons: they were inaccessible, or their trees were unmarketable, or the land was unsuitable for agriculture at the time the land nearby was being cleared. Using these patches as indicators of the forests of the time would be like making assumptions about the quality of furniture made in the seventeenth century by examining a rickety chair that's been collecting dust for centuries in a farmhouse attic. It's not by accident that it has been set aside.

There is no photographic record, of course, so we rely on eyewitness observations made at that time for an accurate picture of the forest. Some fascinating work has been done by forest ecologists associated with Hubbard Brook Experimental Forest in central New Hampshire and Harvard Forest in central Massachusetts, who have "reconstructed" the presettlement forest by noting the relative frequency of mention of particular species. They do this by looking at the town lotting records made by the surveyors who laid out the towns, and tallying the

Figure 1.2 Hardwood stands above the bold line are dominated by beech; below the line, oak is the dominant hardwood.
Courtesy of Charles Cogbill.

various species cited in the descriptions. These records from the time of European settlement show that oak dominated the southern hardwood forests, while beech dominated those in the north. The transition zone between the two is shown in Figure 1.2. White pine was common in the river valleys but not in the uplands. Spruce was a common component in the mixedwood forests and much more present in the northern hardwood forests than it is today.

Except for the use of fire by Indians in the valleys, particularly in southern New England, changes in the forest came about through nature's own management tools:

wind, including the occasional hurricane, ice, early-season snow, and lightning-sparked fire.

It is safe to say that the forest had trees much larger and older than it has in most places today, that the forest floor was littered with boles and limbs of fallen trees rotting into the soil, and that the forest duff layer was deep and laden with moisture.

THE PASTORAL ENTERS THE WILDERNESS

This vast, rich land was claimed by England, France, and Holland, who fought to control the territory that would become Quebec and Canada's Maritime Provinces, New England, and New York. Land was granted by kings to their relatives or proprietors. The economic interests of the proprietors and the crown were served by selling off or granting wilderness tracts to people willing to build settlements on land controlled by Indians. To harvest the New World's seemingly infinite riches, the land needed to be occupied, and transportation systems into the interior—waterways and roads—needed to be developed. Across the Northeast, European settlement spread from the coast up the valleys of the major rivers: the Hudson, Connecticut, Merrimack, Kennebec, and Penobscot.

Timber and furs were shipped to a Europe whose forests were mostly gone, having largely been converted to agriculture. After the American Revolution and the rising of a new nation, the land grants continued, though the grantors were the new state and federal govern-

Figure 1.3   An image of an early settler clearing a homestead in 1740, from the Harvard Forest Dioramas, Fisher Museum, Harvard Forest, Petersham, Massachusetts. *Photo by John Green.*

ments, which were short of funds but rich in land. Debts to military officers were paid off through grants of land. It was crucial to the strength and security of the new nation that the land get settled, a policy that resulted in people owning property who never could have done so in the country of their ancestors. Given that the settlers had their roots in a seventeenth- and eighteenth-century Europe in which only the wealthy owned land, it was truly revolutionary to start over in the New World with a system that encouraged common men to own land. The people working the land in the Northeast weren't just tenant farmers renting land from the nobility; they owned it, and the fruits of their labors were their own.

At that time, progress was universally defined as the domestication of land, the process of beating back the wilderness and replacing it with productive farms. For this to become a nation, the forest had to give way to farmland to grow crops. Settlers felled the forests and used the wood for a number of purposes. Because pine and spruce grow straight and are easily worked, they were used for building houses and barns. Though some hardwood was used in making furniture and farm equipment, it had value mainly as fuel for domestic cooking and heating as well as for commercial production of potash. In areas where there were iron deposits, hardwoods were smoldered into charcoal to smelt the ore.

Making potash was a clever means of finding some quick cash in all the wood that a settler had to remove from his potential cropland. Nearly every settler burned the hardwoods and collected the ashes. The ashes were then leached with water to make lye. The lye was then boiled, and the residue dried into potash. Thirty cords of wood (an acre could produce that many cords) would produce a ton of ashes. A ton of ashes would produce 1/6 of a ton of potash, which was worth $10 or so (a ton of potash sold for $60 to $80). Clearing land could thus provide a one-time bonus of $10 per acre, a nice return on what had to be gotten rid of. Adjusted for inflation (from 1800), that would be a windfall of $337 per acre.

There was no market for hardwood trees, and if there had been, it would have been difficult to transport them, because unlike softwood, hardwood logs don't float, and the only viable means for moving logs any distance was by river drives.

As agriculture took over, stones were removed from new cropland and piled into walls that separated the cropland from adjacent pastures. Wolves and mountain lions were extirpated to make the land safe for livestock and people.

ACCELERATED CHANGE

The clearing of the land signaled both a change of ownership and a change of use. The Northeast had been a heavily forested land that was lightly settled by Indians, whose social economy depended on a combination of farming and hunting/gathering. The forest provided most of what they needed for daily life. The new occupants had a different model, an agrarian one, and the forests had to fall for their population to prosper and grow.

After decades—in some places, it took generations—subsistence agriculture shifted to commercial agriculture as farmers grew livestock, grain, and other food for sale, mostly to urban markets. As the economy grew, production of lumber also moved from subsistence to commercial, and demands on the forest increased. By the 1820s, the forest covered only 30 percent of the landscape.

When developing a road system, builders often followed the path of least resistance, which meant river valleys. Clearing banks and straightening rivers to accommodate roads had long-lasting negative effects on many river ecosystems.

In the domestication of the wilderness, some species of plants and animals were lost, while many new species were introduced from Europe. Some of these—dandelions, Queen Anne's lace—have been benignly absorbed into the landscape. Others, however, including some more recent arrivals, have been so effective at gaining a foothold—Japanese knotweed and non-native phragmites, honeysuckles, and buckthorns, for instance—that they are threatening native species.

The large ungulates—elk, caribou, and moose—were extirpated by overhunting, and the white-tailed deer nearly so. Beavers, prized for their felt for hats, were trapped so extensively that they—and the pond-meadow cycle they engineered—were rare by the 1850s, a wholesale change of ecosystem in a relatively short period of time.

This tale of wholesale environmental change in the service of progress should ring a contemporary bell. Today, many people are understandably concerned over the accelerated cutting and conversion of the world's rainforests. By cutting lush Brazilian, Malaysian, and Indonesian forests, important ecosystems with rich biological diversity are being sacrificed for food production and settlement. Accompanying this wave of investment and settlement are blows to indigenous peoples through a conversion of what was communal land to new ownership. Despite the cautions from those nations who already have been through the process, developing nations find it difficult to accept limits to growth, because the booming economy brings prosperity to many impoverished people.

That summarizes the nearly identical process by which the northeastern United States was settled in the two centuries following the landing at Plymouth, Massachusetts. Natural resources in remote, undeveloped nations can seem limitless, there for the taking. As this nation pressed westward, the rich prairie soils on inexpensive land drew many second- or third-generation farmers happy to abandon their stony hill farms in the Northeast. In the mid-nineteenth century, the rural areas of the Northeast lost a large percentage of their population, some to the cities and some to the West. They left behind a changed landscape.

It was at this time that George Perkins Marsh wrote an influential book, *Man and Nature*, that called attention to the calamity that had been created by the land clearing and the agricultural practices of that time. Marsh, whom many people think of as the founder of the environmental movement, preached a gospel of watershed protection and reforestation that he developed from observing environmental degradation in the countries of the eastern Mediterranean. When he saw it happening in his native Vermont, too, he started planting trees.

Planting trees has certainly played a part in bringing the forest back to the Northeast. But what Marsh didn't realize at that time is that the Northeast has resilient soils and forests. Conditions here weren't as dire as those in more arid regions. In most of the Northeast, it's a given that when agricultural land is abandoned, the forest grows back.

Natural reforestation is an inexorable process, and our understanding of that process is a foundation of the silviculture that's practiced in the region today. Forest succession begins anew with cropland and pastures seeding in with species such as aspen, paper birch, and white pine. The forests that come back from abandoned cropland or pastureland, as they have been doing parcel by parcel for generations, are much less complex than those of the pre-settlement landscape. It takes generations—of trees, not just of humans—for the complexity to return.

There have also been losses of species along the way. Chestnut and elm are no longer forest trees, victims of introduced pathogens from Europe. Many native animals and plants are gone, replaced by

Figure 1.4 The logging crew of the Santa Clara Lumber Company, circa 1910.
Courtesy of the Adirondack Museum.

opportunistic newcomers. It's a different ecosystem, and the changes go beyond just diminished species diversity.

BLANK SPOTS ON THE MAP

This sketch of the history of land use holds true for much, but not all, of the Northeast. Some areas were never farmed, never settled in that way, because they were inaccessible: either too swampy or too mountainous, or both, like the Adirondacks. The histories of New York's Adirondacks, Vermont's Northeast Kingdom, New Hampshire's North Country,

and Maine's unorganized territories are much more influenced by timber extraction than by agriculture.

The Adirondacks continued to be remote even after lands farther to the west were settled. The forbidding vast swamps interspersed with rugged mountains managed to thwart most settlers attempting to bring in agriculture. The margins of this region were settled, and some towns sprang up, but the interior remained a blank spot on the map well into the early nineteenth century.

Timber was a resource to remove and sell. This was a strictly utilitarian view of land. Although some attention was paid to the beauty inherent in the ruggedness of the landscape, the land was valued for what it held: timber. Pine and spruce had value for building materials, so loggers actively sought these species. In the Adirondacks and Catskills, hemlock bark was ground up and used for tanning hides into leather. As in the areas cleared for farming, the hardwoods had little value. That is, unless there were iron deposits in the area. If so, all the hardwood within reach was made into charcoal, which was used in both furnaces and forges to process iron. Charcoal also was the raw material for chemicals including alcohols, aldehydes, ketones, and other organic compounds.

White pine was valued everywhere it grew. The wood is light in weight but relatively strong, and the volume of wood in even a young tree is phenomenal. As any woodworker knows, pine is easy to work. Its use for masts for the King's navy has become the stuff of legend, contributing to the false impression that white pine was a huge component of the forest. That was true almost nowhere, except in the valleys of the major rivers. In the uplands, it was 3 percent or less of the forest.

Pine went first, and when it became hard to find, lumbermen's attention turned to spruce, which was the next best thing. Spruce was much more common. It grew in pure stands in swamps and on spruce flats, and was a major component of mixedwood forests.

Entry into the blank spot on the map came through the unlikely pairing of commercial logging and wilderness recreation. Between 1840 and 1890, Adirondack guides

Figure 1.5 An Adirondack guide and his client, known as a "sport." No points awarded for correctly guessing which is the guide and which is the sport. *Courtesy of the Adirondack Museum.*

transporting well-heeled "sports" into the wilderness to hunt deer and fish for trout accounted for much of the traffic into the interior. Lumber companies bought land from the state for pennies per acre and logged the spruce and pine. With all the commercial value extracted from the land, there was little point in paying taxes on it, so ownership of abandoned tracts reverted to the towns.

Similarly, in New Hampshire, the White Mountains saw the twin uses of logging and tourism. Hotels sprang up on lake shores and in the mountains, while loggers cut the backcountry woods and cut them hard. By 1890, 832 sawmills were operating in New Hampshire, and 17 logging railroads crisscrossed the state. Water was the other prominent means of transport, and loggers built dams to hold back a pond full of logs, then let them loose in the spring.

There was a parallel history in the remote sections of Maine, with sporting camps and logging being the rule in the backcountry. A map of Maine today makes the point very clearly as it shows that most of the towns in what has come to be known as the unorganized territories have never been named. Instead, the towns are referred to by location on a grid, as in T16 R5 WELS, which means Town 16 Range 5 West of the East Line of the State.

In the mid- to late nineteenth century, timber barons like David Pingree, J. E. Henry, and George Van Dyke were aggregating land all across the North Country. In many cases, these holdings became the core of the paper companies, which began to be powerful forces.

THE PUBLIC TAKES NOTICE

These remote timberlands were being stripped of anything of commercial value, and the process compromised soils and streams. River flow volumes were so disrupted that downstream mills operated by waterpower were left without power for much of the year. Softwood slash left behind provided fuel for devastating forest fires that plagued the Northeast in the decades before and after the turn of the twentieth century.

From the start, very little land had been left in government ownership. But the public's increasing sensitivity to the abuses of the land was about to change that. The movement started by George Perkins Marsh was gaining traction, which resulted in an interest in public ownership of important lands. In 1885, New York purchased and set aside a million acres of timberland in the Catskills and in the Adirondacks to protect downstream drinking water. In New Hampshire, after decades of fires in the mountains and low flows in the Merrimack, a coalition of tourism interests and downstream mill owners short of water power pressed the case for action against the timber companies and lobbied for public ownership. In 1911, the Weeks Act was signed into law, which allowed the federal government to purchase lands as forest reserves. The White Mountain National Forest was established in 1918 (though land for it was purchased as early as 1914) and today has grown to nearly 800,000 acres. The Green Mountain National Forest would follow in the early 1930s. States also began accumulating parcels of land for state forests and state parks.

Particularly in the Adirondacks, much of what became public land had been abandoned by its owners because it would be decades before timber could be harvested again. Property taxes went unpaid, and towns were carrying many abandoned properties on their tax rolls. Seeing an opportunity to receive some income from these abandoned properties, many towns sold the parcels to the state or federal government with the promise of receiving payments in lieu of taxes. The vast majority of the 17 percent of the Northeast that currently is in public ownership came about in this turbulent period of the public's response to the lack of responsible stewardship of the land.

Farm abandonment continued in much of the region through the 1950s, giving rise to thousands of acres of new forests. Many rural towns reached their lowest populations since European settlement, and farmhouses and farmland found new owners, many of them from away. The back-to-the-land movement beginning in the 1960s brought in thousands of newly rural people. Meanwhile, work in the woodlots continued to be done according to the time-honored tradition: loggers only cut trees of a high-enough quality to have a sawlog in them. Taking only the best trees left many woodlots made up primarily of poorly formed trees.

This discussion of forest history is not meant as a call to self-flagellation. Nor is it an excuse for the rampant overuse of the land. Those were different times, with different societal needs, different standards for land use, and different understandings of implications and effects.

Historical perspective provides a context for understanding the tremendous value of what we have now. The good news is that after many decades of recovery time, much of that forestland now holds stands of large trees. These are not old-growth forests by any means, but many thousands of acres have grown up into stands of very valuable timber. We are blessed in the Northeast to have forests that have such remarkable resilience.

WHO OWNS THE WOODS TODAY?

In the past couple of decades, millions of acres of forestland in the Northeast have changed hands. Exactly how many acres is difficult to determine because a number of the large parcels have been sold more than once. A good board game could be developed—let's call it North Woods Shuffle—in which a player would call out a piece of land and its owner in 1990 and the other players would guess who owns it today. Extra points could be given for correctly naming the intermediate owners.

The general trend is that the paper companies have sold land they'd owned for generations. In the past, paper companies were vertically integrated, controlling all aspects of the process from harvesting timber to processing pulp and making paper. Most of them amassed huge expanses of land in the northern stretches of the Northeast. For example, at its height, Great Northern owned 2 million acres of Maine's woods. If the land had been in one square block—and it wasn't—each of its four sides would have been 56 miles long.

A look at the changing face of Champion International Corp. will give you the picture. In the early 1990s, its holdings were spread across the four northern states: 730,000 acres in Maine, 171,000 in New Hampshire, 130,000 in Vermont, and 325,000 in New York. The company sold much of that land in 1997 to timberland investment companies and to the state and federal governments. Three years later, Champion was gone, merged into International Paper (IP), which already owned plenty of its own land in the Northeast. IP is the largest forest products company in the world and has long been a major player in the Northeast. But by 2007, IP no longer owned any large tracts in the Northeast; it had itself sold off all of its holdings.

IP was just one of many paper companies to recognize that it wasn't necessary to own land; they could just as easily buy their wood from the same lands if someone else owned them. And from an accounting standpoint, it made little sense to keep land that had been bought long before at bargain basement prices—much better to turn that asset into cash. Paper companies were happy to get acreage off their balance sheets, and new investors were happy to get large tracts of land at prices that started at half the value of the timber growing on it.

Who owns the land now? The new owners include a mix of government, conservation organizations, modern-day timber barons, and the new big player, timberland investment management organizations, known as TIMOs.

To generalize, the paper companies have sold their land across the Northeast to TIMOs. These investors are by no means homogeneous. John Hancock, the insurance giant, is one of the larger players, investing on behalf of its pension funds. Other TIMOs pool the assets of institutional investors, and still others represent families and other wealthy investors. Their strategies for making money likewise differ. Some conduct extensive timber harvests in the early years to help pay for the purchase, alarming environmental activists in the process. Others practice a lighter touch through silviculture that focuses more on improving the quality and value of the current standing timber. In most if not all cases, the length of their ownership is predetermined and relatively short, with 10 or 12 years a typical expected tenure. This ongoing turnover is troubling to many people concerned about the long-term conditions on the land.

In most cases, after the paper company sold the land, its relationship with the TIMO buyer continued, as terms of the transaction often included a long-term timber supply contract. The buyers agree to provide a certain volume of wood to the mill at a certain price. Often, the foresters who have been managing the paper company lands find jobs with the new owners.

Public concerns over subdivision and development of these holdings has, in some cases, resulted in a TIMO (and less often the paper company) selling development rights to its land. These agreements, called conservation easements, separate the development rights from the other ownership rights and place them with the state or with a land trust designed to hold them in perpetuity. The owners can continue to manage the land for timber according to agreed-upon standards and engage in other profit-making activities, but they no longer have the right to develop lakefront lots and other desirable small parcels.

The paper industry has changed in other ways as well. As of 2011, not a single paper mill is operating in Vermont, and New Hampshire's largest mill in Berlin has closed and re-opened several times. A substantial (but diminished) paper industry exists in Maine and New York, though most of the names have changed. Gone are St. Regis, Great Northern, Georgia-Pacific, Boise Cascade, Scott Paper, and Champion. The new companies include Katahdin, NewPage, Verso, and SAPPI. Competition from Europe, Asia, and South America has hurt the owners of the northeastern mills, many of whose vintage makes them antiques. Whether the current mill owners continue to invest in their manufacturing plants and equipment will determine whether papermaking continues to be a viable industry in the Northeast.

FAMILY FORESTS

The land that was never settled and farmed is mostly in the hands of TIMOs and, in some cases, government agencies or conservation organizations. Much of it has been conserved. The threat of development has been forestalled, and the land remains in relatively large parcels. The huge ownership changeover on the former industrial lands has been an easily observed reality because each sale has played prominently in the pages of local newspapers.

Less visible but perhaps even more significant to the future of the region's forest is the ongoing dramatic change in the ownership of the smaller holdings. Let's shift attention to the current state of the land that was settled, farmed, and then saw the livestock leave and the forest return over the course of a hundred or so years.

Nearly half of the 51 million acres of forestland in New England and New York is owned by individuals or families. Corporate owners hold 17 million acres, or one-third of the forestland, while individuals and families own 25 million acres. In forest policy circles, the latter owners are known as non-industrial private forest owners or NIPFs, an unglamorous term that we will try our best to avoid. What once were known as woodlots, we'll call family forests.

In the last comprehensive survey conducted by the U.S. Forest Service in 2006, there were 446,000 family forests of 10 or more acres in the Northeast. Slightly more than a million families own 1 to 9 acres. As forests are subdivided and sold from Buffalo to Fort Kent, the average size of a family forest is inexorably decreasing. Across the seven-state region, the average holding of forestland is 29 acres. Because of the constantly changing ownership, it's difficult to get a snapshot of who owns the non-industrial forestland, but it's clear that the demographics of forest ownership have changed dramatically from the time when they were mostly woodlots owned by farmers.

Across the region, there are many thousands of new owners of family forests. This has resulted in an even greater change to the landscape—both physical and cultural—because many of these people are building houses and moving in. There are a number of reasons for this:

Safe haven. The flight to the country from urban and suburban areas was well under way before the attacks of September 11, 2001, suddenly made urban life seem altogether too perilous for many. A house in the country became attractive, and often that house in the country came with acreage. There are many thousands of these "accidental owners" of forestland—they didn't set out to buy a forest, they were interested in privacy and a quiet life in the country.

Land values. In the middle decades of the twentieth century, forestland was valued at a price near the value of its standing timber. As the rural areas began to take on more of a recreational value, prices increased. And despite the occasional short-duration stagnant periods, the price of land has continued to increase. Still, for people accustomed to the cost of real estate in urban and suburban areas, rural acreage seems almost laughably affordable. On the other hand, for the children of long-time residents who participate only in the local economy, today's prices can make it nearly impossible to own land.

Digital age. In the age of cell phones and high-speed internet connections, people increasingly are working from home offices, and those home offices no longer need to be in Westchester County, New York, or the Boston suburbs. This has allowed formerly urban professionals to make a living in very rural places.

Intergenerational shift. Traditionally, land has been owned by older people, and that remains true today. What's different is the extent to which that is true. The average age of a family forest owner in the Northeast is more than 60. Seventy percent of the landowners are 55 or older, and half of those are over 65. That means that we are at the beginning stage of a remarkable transfer of ownership of forestlands, because much of the land held by older people will be sold to new owners or bequeathed to a new generation.

These factors are combining to repopulate the rural areas gradually with people with a more urban or suburban background. What this means to the local culture is being played out at school board and planning commission meetings across the Northeast. It is also being played out in the forests. Instead of owning rural land for traditional uses such as farming and logging, newer owners are more likely to value it for its privacy, its beauty, and its cross-country ski trails. For many, it's hard to imagine having chainsaws and log trucks on their land. For others, actively harvesting firewood, making improvements in wildlife habitat, and doing other hands-on projects can be a tremendously satisfying pastime.

Some people are enthusiastic about the rewards of managing their forestland—most likely those who have grown up with a chainsaw in the family and an interest in procuring firewood. They identify themselves as forest owners, perhaps proudly post a Tree Farm sign, and may belong to their state's association of forest landowners. Those people, known in forestry circles as "the choir," are a

tiny fraction of the region's forest owners. That's true despite the fact that in
each of the states in the Northeast, the
state's forestry division and Cooperative
Extension for decades have been actively
encouraging family forest owners to join
these organizations.

Why do so few of the million or so
owners of family forests belong to these
forestry organizations? It's because most
of these family forest owners don't define
themselves that way—they just happen to
own some forest. Maybe they inherited a
piece of land, or forestland was included
when they purchased their house. In other
words, they didn't set out to buy a forest,
but now they own one.

Is there a prototypical family forest
owner? It would be just as difficult to identify a typical American. Dozens of surveys
of family forest owners have been conducted in an attempt to understand their
attitudes about owning land. The surveys
generally show that people own land for
the quiet and the beauty it provides, for
the recreational opportunities it presents,
and for the wildlife that live there. Being
able to see and hear wildlife is invariably
high on the list. Very few people, on the
other hand, say that timber harvesting
is their primary reason for owning land.
Most forest owners don't see themselves
as a source of fiber for the timber industry. At the same time, nearly all surveys
show that most family forest owners are
not necessarily averse to timber harvesting, and that they would get involved in it
under the right circumstances.

THE STEWARDSHIP IMPERATIVE

We've come a long way from the days
when land had so little value that many
people stopped paying the property tax
on it and let it revert to the town. Even
up until the early 1960s, the value of land
was tied directly to its capacity to generate income, and land with timber on
it sold for a price that was close to the
value of that timber. The underlying land
itself wasn't considered a significant part
of the calculation.

Today, it's just the opposite. Land has
appreciated tremendously in value. Except
for parcels that are measured in hundreds
of thousands of acres, the timber value
of a property is a small part of its market
value. In 2011, despite years of a stagnant
economy, it would be difficult to find a 50-
acre parcel of accessible (not landlocked)
forestland (even if lacking mature trees)
for less than $1,000 an acre.

That creates quite a challenge: how can
you simultaneously take good care of the
forest and cut enough wood to cover the
costs of owning it? Given the steep costs
of buying in and the substantial ongoing
costs of ownership—property tax and
maintenance, for instance—a family forest
is no longer capable of producing enough
revenue to justify considering it solely an
investment in timber. But, as we mentioned,
most of today's family forest owners aren't
in it for the timber income alone.

At this moment in history, large societal
concerns could usher in a golden age of
forest stewardship. Our interest in gaining independence from foreign oil and our
concern over global climate change have

sparked a renewed interest in our first fuel, wood. Research into ways to turn wood into various forms of energy—heat, electricity, and fuel for engines—addresses both of these problems. Increasingly, it is viewed as both environmentally sound and patriotic to use wood, to burn it cleanly, to use it wisely, and to make sure it's used within a short distance of where it was grown. This renewed interest in wood as a fuel source has been accompanied by cautions about overuse of the resource, and there is a healthy ongoing debate about the ways the complex ecosystem can be sustained while wood is removed from it for human use.

Family forest owners have an opportunity to participate in stewarding this valuable resource. Our forests, despite a long history of exploitive use, are not something to be squandered, but rather a boon to be nurtured. Land ownership, whether accidental or not, provides the opportunity for people to learn the great pleasures of tending a piece of land, improving its capacity for wildlife, increasing the value of its crop of wood, ensuring that it protects water quality and quantity, and guaranteeing that it plays its role in purifying the air and sequestering carbon.

We as individuals make choices every day. Not managing land is a choice, and it's a perfectly valid choice. Not every acre needs to be harvested, and not every parcel needs to have active forest management. Letting nature roll along without our direct intervention does no harm to the forest. If someone tells you they want to help you improve the forest's health by thinning your trees, or that your forest needs to be cut because it's stagnating, know that it's almost always an economic argument and not a forest health argument. Trees and forests can do perfectly fine without our intervention. Choosing not to do any logging can be a better choice than doing it poorly. And it's a much better choice than dividing the forest into house lots and converting it to non-forest.

Yet if you don't manage your forest, you miss the chance to really get to know it. There's nothing quite like learning a piece of land so completely that no matter where you are on it, you feel at home. There's nothing like becoming a significant part of the history of a piece of land.

By taking an active role, you also can improve many aspects of the land—the value of its timber, its usefulness for recreation, its capacity to provide suitable conditions for numerous species of wildlife. If you take the first steps, you may quickly see the many rewards for doing a good job—heating your house with your own wood, introducing a child or grandchild to nature, walking on trails that result from a harvest, paying the property tax bill with proceeds from a timber sale. And there's nothing more special than stopping by a stream and knowing that it's as pure as water can be.

Many people throughout the ages have taken great satisfaction from acting on their impulse to leave their piece of ground a better place than when they came to it. And there are many beneficiaries now and in the future of those actions taken today. ◘

CHAPTER 2

THE BIG PICTURE

What's the difference between a field and a forest?

No, it's not a riddle, it's a real question worth pondering. In a field, the dominant plants are grasses and forbs, unlike the trees that define a forest. These field plants are not as tall as trees, and they're cut down more often: if the field is managed by a farmer for hay, it's mowed at least twice a year. Even if it's being maintained simply to retain some open land—maybe it provides a stunning view of what's beyond it—it will likely be brush-hogged every few years.

Another difference is that when you walk in a field on a sunny summer day, you need sunglasses and you feel the heat. Leave the field and step into the forest and you'll need to take off your shades to see in the filtered light, and you'll enjoy the refreshing cool air.

Sure, there are lots of other differences we could discuss—a hayfield is less complex in its vertical dimensions than any forest, for instance—but let's move on to the similarities between them. The plants in each are of many different species, unless it's cropland or a plantation established as a monoculture. If you walk through a field that shows off as a sea of dandelions in May, you'll probably find plenty of timothy and clover and vetch interspersed with the dandelions. (That species mix is true if it's a regularly fertilized hayfield. Otherwise, it might tend to have more goldenrod, hawkweed, and sheep sorrel.) Like a forest, a field also provides a home to a wide variety of animals: insects, birds, mammals, and reptiles. If you don't believe me, visit a hayfield on the day that it's mowed, and see what predators show up to take advantage of all the suddenly exposed prey animals. Hawks, in particular, have an affinity for tractors pulling haybines, and after the equipment is shut down or moved to the other end of the field, you might also see a fox or a coyote hunting rodents.

A field is a forest waiting to happen. In any area of the Northeast that has an agricultural history, most of the forestland was once either cropland or pasture. A hayfield or pasture that is left unmown or uneaten for three years or more will be well on its way to making the transition to a forest, and you'll see the first saplings of white pine or aspen or paper birch poking their tips out above the grass. Depending

Figure 2.1 White pine will colonize a field if there is a nearby seed source. Its seeds succeed even better on bare ground.

on conditions, they'll seed in sparsely or thickly, and before long the bright, warm, open land will start experiencing some shade. Here in the Northeast, the natural tendency for most land is to grow trees, and they will regenerate on their own without our help.

This regeneration has major implications for forest management in our region. Let's compare it to the forestry practices in other parts of the United States. In the South, loblolly pine is the most valuable species, and though it can regenerate naturally, more often it is grown in plantations. Tree farmers plant it, thin it

twice, harvest it, and then repeat the process. These rotations (the time span from planting to final harvest) can be as short as 20 years. In the Northwest, the other great lumber-producing region, the process is similar but the preferred species are Douglas fir and western hemlock, and the rotations are longer. In these regions, forestry has come to rely on replanting trees. It's not that other trees won't self-seed, but those that do—primarily slower-growing hardwoods—are not valuable commercial species. Even the valuable species have been genetically improved so that natural regeneration of Douglas fir and western hemlock is discouraged. On the other hand, the Northeast is blessed with a mix of native hardwood and softwood species, nearly all of which are worth growing. Pine and spruce have been planted in the Northeast, but it happens rarely today. Industrial forests have relied less on planting in recent decades, and the bulk of our planted forests are from the 1930s, when the Civilian Conservation Corps and the Soil Conservation Service planted thousands of acres. This means we are mostly surrounded by a self-regenerating natural forest.

A DYNAMIC SYSTEM

The birth of a forest is a dynamic time—everything is changing, and it happens quickly enough that we can observe it in our lifetimes. It doesn't require time-lapse photography to recognize that trees are taking over an uneaten pasture. The dynamic nature of a forest also doesn't end when a forest develops a full, high canopy. Even though the term "climax forest" might suggest that it's static, it's not. A forest doesn't settle into a steady state. It is an ever-changing system.

Although trees are the dominant plants and the defining characteristic of a forest, they are but one part of a highly complex system that includes a rich and changing assemblage of organisms—plants, animals, bacteria, fungi, algae—all interacting with each other and with the physical environment—the air, soil, rocks, and water—in which they exist. We can come up with lists of the components of a forest. We can name, for instance, the species of songbirds that are native, and we can count the mammals and the reptiles and the amphibians. It's much more difficult, however, to catalog the microorganisms—the bacteria, the fungi, the slime molds—that inhabit the soil and wood that's decomposing. The system comprising all of these plants, animals, and microbes churns along, with each individual organism present or absent depending on whether a particular set of conditions exists. The plants and animals are interrelated in a web of life and death that is never static and is unique from forest to forest, acre to acre.

The interactions among these elements—competition, predation, nutrient cycling, parasitism, symbiosis—are what make forests the truly fascinating places they are. In this way, a forest may be better defined as a verb than a noun, understood by what it does rather than what it is.

As our understanding of the interactions and the processes has increased, the practice of forestry has evolved to take this knowledge into account. As it does, foresters strive to bring that knowledge to the heart of how we manage these forests. Forestry has evolved so much in recent decades that you can no longer use the term forest management without having it imply the management of all the elements of the forest—the trees, of course, but also the soils, the water, the other plants, and the animals. When you manage a forest, you are managing the whole system.

This is a humbling notion: that by managing a particular forest for one purpose or another, we also are managing—whether by design or inadvertently—the animals that live there. It's daunting to understand that unless appropriate precautions are taken, we are also affecting rivers and streams and the life that depends on them. All of our decisions have implications beyond the decision to cut a specific tree for the sawlogs, pulpwood, and firewood it contains. That responsibility shouldn't paralyze us, it should make us proceed with appropriate humility.

LIFE AND DEATH

The cycles in a forest include that of life and death, in which organisms benefit from—and sometimes cause—the demise of other organisms. In a complex ecosystem, this process is going on throughout the system at all times. It is inevitable, unavoidable, and utterly natural.

Over the eons of their coexistence, trees, insects, and fungi negotiated a deal that worked well. In this deal, they all got what they needed: lifespans of a reasonable duration for individuals of a species combined with assurance of the continuance of the species itself. Despite the occasional flareup when conditions favored a particular insect or fungus and things looked bad for the trees, the players in this drama managed to keep to the agreement and co-existed successfully for a long time.

Figure 2.2   Forest tent caterpillars strike when leaves should be at their best; the center tree is nearly denuded of leaves. *Photos courtesy of Bugwood.org.*

In the battle between a tree and a scale insect, most of us would wish for the tree's success. In this case, our hearts are with Goliath because, despite his size advantage, he can seem particularly vulnerable in other ways. Trees are immobile, for instance, rooted in place and unable to escape a swarming adversary. And reinforcements don't appear immediately in time of need because tree reproduction is relatively slow—trees can't reproduce on a weekly basis, as some insect adversaries can. Trees are, however, far from helpless and have proven quite able to defend themselves from the insects and diseases that have co-existed with them for thousands of years. It's all part of the agreement.

In the grand scheme of things, it's not desirable for individual trees to live forever; disease and death are an integral part of a healthy forest. Sometimes tree death arrives a little early, but if we keep in mind that the agents of death are themselves forms of life—subject to all the constraints faced by every other creature—we are free to marvel at the complex interrelationships that make the forest an endlessly interesting environment.

Let's look at one example of this sort of relationship. The forest tent caterpillar, *Malacosoma disstria,* eats leaves—lots of them. It's not the adult moths but the larvae that do the damage, and they fare best on sugar maple, though they're perfectly happy with red oak and other hardwoods. You've probably seen the gruesome sight of a forest defoliated by these caterpillars. They strike in June, eating new leaves, which should at that time be at their lush,

green best. Instead, the caterpillars render the leaves skeletal, and it can seem unlikely that the trees will recover. Still, they usually do, putting out new leaves within a few weeks. The same destruction may occur the next year, and perhaps even the year after that. Then the caterpillar's cyclical population surge will be over, and these insects will be hard to find for a decade or more. When you see a leafless forest in June, it's hard not to think of counterattacking, but although these native defoliators can drastically reduce growth rates, amazingly, they rarely kill their hosts.

The forest tent caterpillar is native, and it evolved with its hardwood hosts. It also evolved with a collection of predators, parasites, and diseases that feed on it and bring its booming population to bust. The forest tent caterpillar's cycle is typical of at least eighteen other species of Lepidoptera (moths and butterflies), all of which have somewhat predictable outbreaks. Populations can be high over a broad region, sometimes over most of the United States and Canada, and then will collapse completely for many years, only to rise dramatically again years later, as though they were keeping to a schedule.

Different insects have different preferences, and leaves, buds, fruits, cambium, wood, and roots all offer something to one insect's or another's picky palate. Most insects have adapted to dine on a particular part of a tree or a particular tree species, rendering them incapable of eating anything else. All this feeding turns a tree's carbohydrates into protein-rich fare, and the tree-eating insects in turn feed frogs,

INSECT	Scientific name	Host species	Damage	Native?	Notes
Eastern tent caterpillar	Malacosoma americanum	rose family, especially cherry and apple	defoliator	native	Rarely kills trees. The caterpillars feed early in the year and most trees send out a second batch of leaves so this is mainly an aesthetic problem.
Forest tent caterpillar	Malacosoma disstria	many, but especially sugar maple and aspens in our area	defoliator	native	Populations fluctuate to an extreme degree. Outbreaks can cause widespread defoliation This "tent caterpillar" doesn't make tents.
Gypsy moth	Lymantria dispar	several hundred species, with oak a favorite	defoliator	non-native	Has spread widely and been extremely destructive since arriving from Europe in 1869. A fungus, Entomophaga maimaiga, has limited damage in some situations.
Maple leaf cutter	Paraclemensia acerifoliella	sugar maple	defoliator	native	A late season defoliator, it puts a damper on fall foliage, but isn't usually life threatening. Repeated attacks reduce vigor.
Birch leafminer	Fenusa pusilla	paper birch and gray birch	defoliator	non-native	A wasp imported from the insect's native range has been very effective in limiting this little sawfly. Several other introduced insects also mine birch leaves.
Sugar maple borer	Glycobius speciosus	sugar maple	girdles tree	native	The larva of this beetle chews its way around the tree in a shallow spiral. Its track opens the tree to fungal infection and can lead to breakage.
Emerald ash borer	Agrilus planipennis	all native ash species	girdles tree	non-native	Prolific, consumes cambium and phloem, and has no natural enemies. Discovered in this country in 2002. Introduced from Asia, it has spread rapidly. All our ash species are susceptible.
White pine weevil	Pissodes strobi	white pine, Norway spruce	eats terminal bud	native	When the terminal shoot is killed, side branches compete for dominance, causing distorted growth and timber value that's reduced, sometimes to zero.

Figure 2.3   These are the most common insects affecting trees in the Northeast.

DISEASE	Scientific name	Species it afflicts	Damage	Native?	Notes
Black knot	*Apiosporina morbosa*	all species in the genus Prunus	fungal cankers disfigure branches	native or non-native	*Very common. Not usually too serious in the forest but can be very destructive in orchards. Occurs throughout North America.*
Beech bark disease	*Cryptococcus fagisuga* (an insect) and *Neonectria faginata* and *N. coccinea* (two fungi)	American beech, primarily	fungus kills cambium	somewhat uncertain	*Non-native scale insect allows a fungus to invade beech trees. One of the two fungi that follows appears to be native. A small percentage of beech trees have some resistance to this disease complex, but most are slowly killed. The disease has changed hardwood forests in the Northeast for the worse.*
White pine blister rust	*Cronartium ribicola*	eastern white pine; other white pines	fungus girdles and kills the tree	non-native	*Like all rust diseases, this fungus needs two host species; in this case the other host is either a currant or gooseberry. Normally, it isn't a terrible problem in the East; western pines are more susceptible.*
Shoestring root rot	*Armillaria*	hundreds of species	fungus some-times girdles and kills tree	native	*There may be more than 30 different armillaria species and they vary in their virulence. Some kill only stressed trees, but others may be more aggressive. Infection can spread from one tree to another by way of fungal bodies that look like shoelaces. Both hardwoods and conifers are vulnerable.*
Eutypella canker	*Eutypella parasitica*	maples	fungal cankers girdle branches	native	*Trees sometimes live for decades with eutypella cankers. The fungus may wreck the timber potential of sugar maples and sometimes weakens the tree so much that it breaks.*

Figure 2.3 (cont.)   These are the most common diseases affecting trees in the Northeast.

salamanders, snakes, birds, numerous mammals, and the many carnivorous insects that populate the six-footed realm. That's quite an assemblage benefiting from some temporary damage to a live tree.

Other organisms specialize in wood that is diseased or already dead. Where would we be without the decomposers that graciously devour fallen trees and turn them back into soil? Picture a forest floor in which fallen leaves, twigs, limbs, and boles accumulate uneaten for decades. Dead plants—and plant and animal parts—would just pile up, and the elements locked in them would not be available for other plants and animals. The sheer variety of life in this system, everchanging at both the micro and the macro level, has a remarkable stability. On any one plot of ground, the plants and animals, microbes and fungi—all the organisms—are in flux, but the internal mechanisms operate according to their intrinsic order. Humans are part of this system, too, and sometimes we act in concert with it and other times in opposition. In many places, our presence and our appetites have altered the arrangement that had been forged over the millennia.

Humans have made wholesale changes to the system. In trying to tame the land for our use, we've cleared forestland and grazed animals on it, made alterations in the forest structure, and shown preference for one tree species over another. It's not as if we set out to disrupt the ecosystem, but that's what happened.

It wasn't some sort of insidious plot. It's just that we humans are part of the system, and our actions have consequences. Political, social, and economic forces are at play as people make decisions about use of the land and its resources. So far, the human part of the system has not been particularly mindful of the enormity of its impacts. We can, through ever-increasing awareness and actions based on that awareness, do a better job of integrating our needs with those of the system as a whole.

NATURAL DISTURBANCE

Nothing perks up a forester's ears at a cocktail party and makes him want to talk shop more than the term "natural disturbance." One reason it's so fascinating is that its effects are so far-reaching. The composition of a forest—the tree species, their age, how densely they coexist—is largely a function of its history of natural disturbance.

Before we delve into how that works, let's take a quick look at the roster of natural disturbances that occur in the forests of the Northeast:

Insects and diseases. Both the most common and the least disruptive of all disturbances, insects and diseases are constantly afflicting scattered single trees everywhere. Without looking for it, you might never notice that a crown is sparse or a bole harbors a canker, signs that slowly but surely, these individual trees are dying.

Fire. Even though every summer brings news of catastrophic fires out West, northeastern forests are not highly prone to fire damage. In fact, the northern hardwood forest, the predominant forest type in the Northeast, has been dubbed "the asbestos forest" because its inherent moisture makes it so difficult to burn. Other forest types in the region are slightly more susceptible, but when someone's backyard brush-pile fire reaches the woods, it tends to stay as a ground fire that doesn't kill trees.

Wind. The range of wind damage is wide. If mild in speed or duration, wind can break off susceptible branches and limbs. If it blows harder or is sustained, it can uproot a tree. Stronger still and it can snap a crown right off a tree. The number of trees affected varies as well, from the single isolated tree that loses a branch in a gust to a swath of many acres in which crowns are snapped off and trees are uprooted by a microburst or downdraft. Even less frequent but with farther-ranging consequences are tornados or straight-line storms.

Snow. The weight of snow on branches can be damaging if it comes when the trees aren't dormant in the early fall or the late spring. Snow collecting on early or late leaves of deciduous trees can break limbs and damage crowns.

Ice. Similar to snow, but capable of wreaking havoc even in dormant trees, ice can weigh down a tree's branches and limbs so they break off. Weather conditions have to be just right for ice to build up and linger on a tree, but when it does, it can affect the crowns of many trees over a wide area. Some areas in the Northeast experienced serious ice storms in 1998 and in 2008 that damaged many tree crowns while not immediately killing many trees.

With a few exceptions, these disturbances tend to kill trees in an area on the order of 2 acres or smaller. They are known as gap disturbances because they result in a gap in the canopy.

In many cases, the gap disturbances result from a tag-team assault. When wind, snow, or ice breaks off a limb, it opens the tree's skin—its bark—to a fungus. Decaying wood attracts insects, which can further compromise the tree's structure. When half the crown snaps off, the tree is just about gone. What killed the tree? Natural disturbance.

Smaller disturbances occur more frequently; snapped branches, for example, occur commonly throughout a stand. Conversely, disturbances that recur less frequently tend to affect larger areas when they do.

Contrasted with gap disturbance is what's known as stand-replacing disturbance. Fire and wind can occasionally destroy entire stands. Rarer still, hurricanes are capable of tremendous destruction. The last hurricane that knocked over stands of trees in every state in New England happened in 1938. Hurricanes are rare in the interior of the Northeast, their frequency determined by proximity to the coast. Researchers from the Harvard Forest estimate that a woodlot located south of a line from Boston to Hartford to central Long Island can expect a major hurricane on average every 85 years. Moving inland, any given spot within central Massachusetts and southern New Hampshire is likely to experience such a blow every 150 years, while a woodlot in southern Vermont or central New Hampshire could expect such an event about every 400 years on average. Pennsylvania and most of New York lie

Figure 2.4 Ice storms have become more common in recent decades. The weight of the ice breaks off limbs and sometimes entire crowns.

to the west of the normal hurricane belt.

Hurricanes can knock down acres and acres of trees. The damage is widespread, but the severity varies because the topography varies so greatly. When a stand blows down, many of the trees are uprooted, excavating craters where the roots once provided an anchor, and leaving the rootwads perpendicular to the ground. Decades later, this pattern in the ground will remain visible. Known as pit and mound, hummock and hollow, or more preciously as pillow and cradle, the presence of this formation indicates that

there has been a history of windthrow in this forest.

WHY DISTURBANCE MATTERS

So far, these disturbances might not seem reason enough for a forester to get all hot and bothered. Wind happens.

True enough. It's the aftermath of the wind that matters.

Let's look at two examples of how disturbance changes a forest. In Forest A, if the disturbance history for the last sixty years has been limited to the occasional

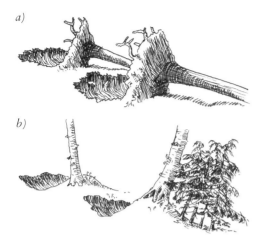

Figure 2.5   a) When a tree is uprooted, it excavates a pit, and the mass of its rootball will disintegrate into a mound over time. *b)* New trees find the mound a hospitable seed bed, and sometimes the rotting log also serves as a nursery.

tree succumbing to insects and disease, then the forest is likely to be made up of relatively large trees forming a more or less continuous canopy. Occasional gaps occur where scattered trees have recently died, and the adjacent trees have not yet expanded their crowns to fill the holes. In those relatively small interruptions in the canopy, more light hits the ground. That means that seeds will sprout, seedlings have the chance to become saplings, saplings can become poles, and on it goes.

Let's imagine that there are places where similar holes in the canopy occurred a couple of decades ago, and the crowns of the larger trees have seized the space in the canopy. Beneath them, the regenerating saplings—if they are the right species—may now be pole-sized trees growing slowly but steadily in diameter and height in the filtered light of the mid-

story. They won't break through into the canopy without another disturbance.

In Forest B, located one ridge to the west, the situation could be quite different. Let's say that ten years ago, it was slammed by a microburst, a disturbance that occurs on average every thirty to fifty years, which caused considerable damage. These straight-line storms—as opposed to the spiraling winds of tornados and hurricanes—can include thunderstorm-spawned downdrafts that leapfrog from one place to another. When they blow through, the sudden burst of high winds can knock down everything in a patch of a few acres. It's a devastating scene: a chaotic tangle of trees either snapped off or uprooted. In Forest B, three separate patches of trees were blown down, opening gaps in the canopy of ½ acre, 1 acre, and the largest, 2 acres. The landowner decided not to bother bringing in a logger to salvage the trees on the ground, so we can see the unaltered consequences of a blowdown.

Figure 2.6   Left to right: seedlings, pole, sawtimber, saplings. Seedlings are smaller than 2 inches in diameter. Saplings are at least 4½ feet tall and up to 4 inches in diameter. Poles are between 5 and 10 inches DBH. Sawtimber denotes a tree at least 11 inches DBH.

introduced species

Given the impressive diversity of trees and shrubs in the Northeast, why would people feel the need to augment it? But augment it they have.

Early on, Scots pine and Norway spruce were brought in to establish new forests to stabilize the soil, as George Perkins Marsh preached. The interest in plantations was reinforced by the loss of topsoil in the Dust Bowl, so the Civilian Conservation Corps planted thousands of acres in the 1930s. The Scots pine did its job holding the soil, but it was a commercial bust, as anyone who owns the remnants of these experiments can attest, perhaps because the seed stock produced trees that resemble corkscrews.

That failed introduction is relatively benign compared to those orchestrated by wildlife managers who saw nothing but the benefits of multiflora rose, autumn olive, barberry, and other fruiting shrubs. Not only would these shrubs control erosion, it was said that they would also provide both food and cover for gamebirds like quail, pheasant, and grouse. Plantings of these exotic shrubs were being promoted by government agencies as recently as the 1980s.

Today, we see that where these species have gained a foothold, they don't let go. They can succeed so mightily that nothing else can grow with them. Try making your way through a hedge of multiflora rose, promoted to unsuspecting landowners as "the living fence," to understand just how pernicious that one is.

Lest the foresters and wildlife managers bear the sole responsibility for the invasion of exotic plants, let's not forget the contribution of well-meaning horticulturists who have given us Morrow's honeysuckle, Norway maple, Oriental bittersweet, and purple loosestrife. Each of these disrupts the natural system, replacing or crowding out native species.

These dramatic changes came about through direct intent, yet it's through some of our inadvertent actions that we've had perhaps the most damaging effect of all. In the name of unfettered trade with Europe and Asia, we have blithely escorted in all sorts of alien insects and fungi, and in doing so we have stressed the normally balanced and resilient relationships between trees and other organisms.

Some introduced insects and diseases fail miserably when brought to a new environment and are never heard from again. Others, however, have thrived in the new conditions, gaining the upper hand and creating terrible mayhem. For instance, we have seen the devastating effect of two different fungus species on such wondrous trees as American chestnut and American elm. Chestnut blight and Dutch elm disease had no such impact on the European trees they had evolved with, but when they arrived in North America, these fungi quickly destroyed native trees that had little resistance to them. A scale insect from Europe has opened up American beech to a fungus that weakens and kills the trees. And we are witnessing the collapse of the butternut to yet another fungus. It has taken only a couple of decades to lose the vast majority of our butternut trees.

Until now, it has been fungi that have proven capable of laying waste to an entire species, but we are now faced with several introduced tree-killing insects—Asian long-horned beetle, hemlock woolly adelgid (introduced from the western United States), and emerald ash borer are the three dangerous and imminent—that together have killed millions of trees that have no defense against them.

Emerald ash borer, *Agrilus planipennis*, poses the most immediate threat. This half-inch-long, metallic-looking beetle was first identified on this continent in southeastern Michigan in July 2002, though by that time it probably had been here for a decade or so. By the end of that year, it was blamed for the death of about five million ash trees.

In its native range in China, Korea, Japan, and other Asian countries, it is just one of thousands of unremarkable common beetles—nothing to be afraid of. Yet all North American ash species are highly susceptible to it; even healthy ash trees are attacked and killed. This beetle has several things going for it: a high reproductive potential, an almost complete lack of natural enemies, and, most important, a host plant with zero resistance to it.

Native organisms have had to tailor their existence to eke out a living. Unfamiliar fungi and insects, like the emerald ash borer on the other hand, seem to arrive with a hand full of wild cards, well-positioned to play a deadly game that their opponents have never played before.

We've had fears about insects before. In particular, the gypsy moth's arrival led people to fear the loss of red oak when the moth began to eat its way through oak stands in the late nineteenth century. Over time, it has proven to be less devastating. Which way will the Asian long-horned beetle and emerald ash borer go? Will they continue to be devastating? Or will an effective counteragent naturally appear or be developed by scientists?

Emerald ash borers are not strong fliers, and they spread quickly only when we give them a boost. There are quarantines in place that restrict the movement of logs in and out of infected zones. Individuals moving firewood are much more difficult to police, though, despite prohibitions on moving firewood more than fifty miles.

The importance of these restrictions cannot be overestimated; a visit to the Burncoat neighborhood in Worcester, Massachusetts, will show how devastating Asian long-horned beetle can be: as many as 30,000 street trees have been destroyed in an effort to contain an outbreak there. ⊙

a)

b)

Figure 2.7   a) In Forest A, a single tree has succumbed and provided space for a handful of seedlings to get started. *b)* In Forest B, the opening made by a windstorm has provided good seeding conditions for more trees of different species.

Today in Forest B there are still trunks lying on the ground, and the branches and limbs have mostly decomposed. The rootwads are still standing tall, and much of the soil has been washed from the roots. In the craters, not much is growing yet in the mineral soil. Elsewhere, many of the saplings that had been in the understory were bent by the weight of the trees that fell on them, but those that weren't flattened have thrived in the increased sunlight. These saplings stand 10 feet tall or more, their crowns full. Interspersed among them are smaller saplings that got their start when their seeds, long dormant in the soil, were warmed by the sunlight now hitting the forest floor. Elsewhere in Forest B—picture it as the doughnut surrounding the hole—the disturbance history is not much different from that of Forest A.

These two types of disturbance—one relatively minor, the other shocking—have changed the conditions in the forest, and the forest has responded to the changes. Whenever tree removal or damage occurs in a stand—whether it's from ice storms, insects, disease, wind, or from logging—the remaining stand will respond by changing in two important ways. Its structure will change, and so will its species composition. The nature of these adjustments depends on the extent of the disturbance.

Before I elaborate on forest structure, let me plant a seed for thought: forest management means that we remove trees through logging. The process is a disturbance that can bear distinct similarities to natural disturbance, with the effects showing up both immediately and over a longer time period. In what ways can forest management mimic natural disturbance, and is there value in doing that? We'll return to that idea in a later chapter.

FOREST STRUCTURE

The disturbances in Forest A and B have affected their structure, which we'll define as the variety and arrangement of trees, both living and dead, standing and downed. As a start, think of structure as the combination of the vertical and horizontal.

Let's assume that both Forest A and B got their starts eighty years ago when a farmer stopped haying and the fields reverted to forest. Even though the trees all seeded in at the same time, they do not all grow at the same rate. With trees, age and size are not the same; small trees are sometimes surprisingly old, and many large trees are surprisingly young. Some trees are genetically superior, some benefit from very local site enrichments, and some just have the good luck to be overlooked by browsing deer and to be spared the wind damage that breaks an immediate neighbor. The result is that these stands are stocked with trees of varying diameters. If it is a mixed-species stand, then it also will develop trees of varying heights, and the canopy will develop multiple layers. When looking at structure, consider also the vertical layering of dead

trees; standing snags and downed woody debris in a range of sizes are vital parts of healthy forests because they provide habitat for a diversity of organisms.

As a stand gets started, becomes established, and develops over time, trees of various species grow and compete with one another. Some survive and grow to their full genetic potential, some survive but with growth below their potential, and those that can't compete die. The character of the stand—its mix of tree species, ages, sizes, and canopy—changes over time as a result. Of course these natural changes in a stand, along with any changes we impose, all influence the value and suitability of the forest for use by humans or wildlife. For any particular use of a stand, whether for producing firewood, veneer, or nesting habitat for chestnut-sided warblers, there is a period within the life of the stand during which its conditions are suitable. Because conditions change, a stand is not continuously

Figure 2.8 This complex forest has lots of leafy vegetation from forest floor to canopy.

suitable for any given use. The duration can be brief for some uses and extended for others.

If the forest regenerated intermittently over a long stretch of time, that forest could contain a mixture not just of different sized trees, but of old, middle-aged, and young trees. These different age classes form upper, middle, and lower canopies, and within each of these layers, some trees grow better than others. This means that even more layers are differentiated within the multiple canopy layers. Picture the three-dimensionality of a forest stand, from the forest floor and the herb and shrub layers, into the understory, and through the canopy to the treetops. See all of that space and the varying amounts of vegetation within it and then look from side to side to see its full horizontal extent. That's stand structure.

A full-canopy forest like Forest A is dense on the horizontal plane at the canopy level. But except where there's been disturbance, it's not particularly dense in the midstory or the shrub layer. Where the pole-sized trees have grown in, their crowns enhance the complexity of the midstory that's otherwise occupied only by tree trunks.

Stands with more complex structures are thought to be more resilient and potentially even more productive. They assuredly provide valuable habitat for a greater diversity of plants and animals than do stands with less structural complexity. While there's no standard way of measuring stand structure, it's often expressed in generalities, such as patchy, dense, or multi-storied.

Natural disturbance changes the forest's structure, and it influences the species composition as well, largely because it affects the light and thus the temperature and amount of moisture. The loss of a single tree leads to different light conditions than the loss of a group of trees. Those different light conditions help determine what species of trees will take over that recently vacated space.

Remember that we started this chapter with a discussion of the difference between fields and forests, one difference being the amount of available light. A large enough disturbance makes a forest like a field in terms of the light availability. Suddenly, the conditions become ripe for the pioneer species, the light-loving species that are known to foresters as shade intolerant. Give them a large, sun-filled opening, and those trees—aspens, white birch, pin cherries—will take over in a hurry.

On the other hand, the species that can get established when a single canopy tree dies are known as shade tolerant trees. Sugar maple, beech, and eastern hemlock can live for decades in the low light of a mature forest and bide their time waiting for an opportunity to break on through.

FOREST SUCCESSION

Ecologists refer to the generalized pattern of changes in species composition over time as forest succession. It's the process by which one assemblage of plants outcompetes and succeeds another as the very presence of one group alters the growing environment in favor of the next. In the absence of natural or human disturbance,

Tolerant	Intermediate	Intolerant
Sugar maple	Yellow birch	Paper birch
American beech	Red oak	Aspens
	White ash	Gray birch
Eastern hemlock	Red maple	Tamarack
	White oak	Hickories
Red spruce	Black birch	Black locust
Balsam fir	White pine	Red pine
Atlantic white cedar		Eastern redcedar
Northern white cedar		Black cherry
White spruce		

Figure 2.9 Tree species delineated by their tolerance to shade.

succession proceeds in a somewhat predictable fashion from intolerant species to tolerant species. As they mature, the intolerant species create conditions in which they cede the ground to tolerant species.

Intolerant species will tend to occupy an available site first, and they will dominate that site for some time. These pioneer species are well suited for rapid colonization: they may produce plentiful, wind-borne seeds or may be capable of exceptionally fast early growth as seedlings. These characteristics confer a competitive advantage over other species that don't spread so quickly or perhaps grow more slowly as seedlings.

Over time, however, things change. Those early-successional pioneers tend to live fast and die young, and they are replaced by other species. This is due to changes in the growing conditions—some of which, like understory light levels—are brought about by the very presence of the early colonizing plants themselves. Trembling aspen, for example, cannot compete in the low light levels of the understory and so it cannot succeed its parent trees. But more shade-tolerant species like sugar maple, for example, compete well and, although they grow more slowly, they last longer and eventually outcompete and outlast the pioneers.

The players in forest succession, and the pace with which the process occurs, depend on several site-specific factors, especially soil, climate, and terrain. Still, the general pattern can be seen without venturing too far from home. It is common to see pastures or hay meadows growing up to weeds and brush after the cows or mowing machines are sold. Those brushy fields of goldenrod and meadowsweet in time become thickets of pioneer species: aspen, gray birch, or maybe white pine. If left alone, those thickets eventually become stands of pole-sized trees. Decades later, the birches are dead on the ground, most of the aspens are snapped in half, and the pines are racing to stay atop the maples and ash that are growing up from below.

If these forests escape major disturbance for long enough, eventually they become dominated by late-successional species, such as sugar maple, American beech, or eastern hemlock. Although these species may barely show up in the early going, they tend to become dominant later in the succession of change. They are capable of living a long time—hundreds of years—without being replaced by other mixes of species. In fact, unlike their

silvics

Patterns of disturbance act over long periods of time to influence the species composition of forests. But that doesn't mean that all of the forests experiencing the same patterns of disturbance would hold the same species—far from it.

Inherent site differences in soils, bedrock, topography, slope, and aspect result in variations in the assemblage of vegetation. Conditions will inherently favor one species or group of species over another. A species' seeds, of course, need to be on site for it to grow there.

Different species are genetically programmed with different abilities to compete for the light, water, and nutrients a site offers. Most trees grow best in fertile soil that's moist but well-drained. On any given site, the species that are found depend on how well each uses or tolerates less than optimal environmental conditions. Trees differ in their competitive abilities.

These species characteristics—the life histories, ecological characteristics, and competitive abilities of trees—are known to foresters as silvics. Think of silvics as our understanding of what each species needs in order to reproduce and grow. This is the foundation of silviculture. It deals with the biological characteristics of trees—how they grow and reproduce—and with the ways their physical environment affects each species' biology. Silvics is an understanding of the collection of traits that determines whether a species is likely to be a strong or weak competitor under any given conditions of its habitat.

If Forest B in our example above is a mixedwood forest on a south-facing slope, the seedlings that regenerate in the small gaps could be aspen, paper birch, or white pine. If instead it's a northern hardwood forest on a north-facing slope currently dominated by sugar maple, the gaps could fill in with yellow birch, white ash, and a strong percentage of sugar maple.

Despite the new burst of available light, this moist, rich site might not be taken over by pioneer species and could continue with the species already present. Shade tolerance, moisture preferences, nutrient needs, regeneration prerequisites—these tree traits are the heart and soul of silvics, which is the heart and soul of silviculture. ☉

fast-growing, short-lived, early-successional counterparts whose seedlings tend to die in the understory, the seedlings and saplings of these late-successional species are very tolerant of shade. This is a crucial silvic trait: late-successional species' seedlings are capable of surviving in the understory and can therefore grow up to replace overstory parent trees that die. When this happens, the forest's mix of species remains relatively constant for many decades.

As we discussed in Chapter 1, almost all of our forests in the Northeast have been logged more than once over the last couple of centuries. Many of them were cleared for agriculture, and most have been subjected to all kinds of storms, fires, blights, and more. That's a lot of disturbance, a lot of change, some natural, some brought about by the hand of man. Even stands that escape such forces for long periods eventually succumb to some form of disturbance. When they do, their vegetative cover is set back to an earlier successional stage, and the process continues anew. The climax forest will one day get a new start. Succession is more of a cycle of varying durations than a straight line with a single endpoint. Forest succession marches on, but it goes around in circles. ▣

CHAPTER 3

A WALK IN YOUR WOODS

I've loved my woods since the day I first walked in them, but my appreciation of them has increased exponentially since I first had a professional forester walk in my woods with me. I was a true neophyte. In my case, my guide was the county forester, and he showed me interesting things I would have missed, asked me thought-provoking questions, and showed me how to read certain indicators of the forest's history. That walk in the woods jump-started my passion for what could be done in them and with them. I have since then hired a consulting forester, who has written a management plan for our woods, overseen timber sales, and been an important partner in managing these woods I love.

It's not just the neophyte who will benefit from a walk in the woods with a professional forester. Even if you can identify most of your trees and animal tracks and birds, a forester offers another set of eyes and an entirely different set of experiences that can help you understand what promise your woods might hold. And if you're serious about doing a good job managing your family forest, you'll benefit from the services of a private consulting forester (for more on the work foresters do, see the sidebar *Forester and Logger: Two Important (and Different) Roles* on page 40).

It's quite possible to learn a lot about forestry from books and workshops and through the painful and exhilarating process of trial and error. Only you know how far you want to go with your own forestry education. I highly recommend learning as much as you possibly can, and I just as highly recommend that you engage a forester to be your partner in management. You might want to start out with what some people call a "woodland exam." You would contract with a forester to spend two to four hours walking the property and producing a brief written report that summarizes the property's current conditions and potential, and then makes some recommendations. This is not a formal inventory, which we'll discuss below, but rather a quick sketch. At a reasonable cost, it can give you a sense of possible next steps in the forest stewardship process.

Having this informed look at the resource is important because just as our desires differ, so does the capacity of a piece of land to satisfy them. It will be

forester and logger: two important (and different) roles

Successful forest stewardship has been likened to a three-legged stool, with each leg—forester, logger, and landowner—playing a crucial role.

In newspaper, radio, and television coverage of forestry, it's almost inevitable that the word "forester" is used to refer to any one of these three. The forester, however, has a very specific role to play.

The forester is the one who makes decisions about which trees are cut and which are left to grow, with all of these decisions based on implementing the landowner's goals for the forest. The complexity of that decision takes into account a knowledge of silviculture, soils, forest ecology, markets, and harvesting equipment and techniques. While some states do not have licensing requirements for foresters, those that do—New Hampshire, and Maine, for instance—require that a practicing forester have a combination of education and experience that meets the state's standards.

Depending on who employs them, foresters' responsibilities will differ.

Government foresters. When they work for government agencies, foresters manage public lands and provide information and guidance to private landowners. In the latter role, these service foresters often are the first contact for many landowners. Employed either by the state forestry department or by the state's land grant university, they can provide information about forestry laws and regulations and the various government programs available to landowners. Service foresters provide an introduction to your land and its possibilities and will offer management advice. They will go on a woods walk with you and provide you with a list of private consulting foresters working in your area. In decades past, it was common for a county forester to mark trees for a timber sale. But in this age of reduced budgets for state natural resource agencies, service foresters are now limited in the amount of on-the-ground guidance they can provide to landowners. Foresters employed by the state's forestry department are involved in administering and enforcing the state's forestry programs and regulations.

Procurement foresters. Some foresters work for sawmills, paper mills, and other wood-using companies, and their job is to procure a steady flow of wood for their employers. They often offer forest management services to landowners, and will draw up management plans and oversee timber sales. But no matter how honorable the company or the forester, it must be recognized that there is an inherent conflict of interest in this relationship because a procurement forester's allegiance has to be to his employer. The procurement forester's first job is to buy wood, not to take care of a landowner's needs.

Consulting foresters. Private consulting foresters work for landowners to manage their forests. These foresters are the best means of ensuring that a landowner knows what he or she is getting into when the skidder and the log trucks enter the woods. As the landowner's agent, the consultant represents the client's interests both in the short term (negotiating a contract with the logger and making sure the contract's conditions are met) and in the long term (deciding which trees to keep to improve the future forest).

Consulting foresters provide a range of services, and many of them can do everything from drawing up the initial forest management plan to helping to plan the conservation of an estate. In between, other work they could complete includes: managing timber sales, appraising land and timber, locating boundaries, and providing information about government programs that assist landowners. Increasingly, foresters are becoming more specialized in their set of skills, and it's crucial that the capabilities of the forester you choose match up well with your needs. Probably the two most common tasks a consultant does for a landowner are preparing a forest management plan and administering a timber sale. These are covered in detail in chapters 5 and 8, respectively. When you hire a consulting forester, you are hiring a contractor, not an employee.

What do these services cost? Some consulting foresters charge for their services at an hourly rate (generally, it is between $40 and $75 an hour) plus expenses. Some charge a flat fee for a particular service. Sometimes, foresters invoice for marking timber on a volume basis, charging a certain amount per thousand board feet. In some cases, foresters are compensated by taking a percentage of the proceeds of the timber sale. Among foresters, the latter has become a controversial subject; some question the ethics of charging a percentage because it links the amount of wood cut with the forester's compensation. That could be seen as giving a forester incentive to mark more trees to be cut. Others point out that nearly any means of determining compensation could contain incentives for an unscrupulous forester to overcharge.

Because of the long-term nature of forest management—with plans covering ten or more years and harvests occurring only periodically—most consulting foresters have dozens, if not hundreds, of clients. In any given year, they perform work for only a small percentage of their clients.

Loggers. Loggers cut the trees and move the wood from the forest to the landing. Often, a logger is involved in marketing the wood. They do their work under the direction of the forester, and they work as a contractor, not as an employee. There may be landowners who are knowledgeable enough about markets and forestry that they can oversee a logging job, negotiate a contract with the logger, and mark the trees to be cut, but unless you have a lot of experience in this, it's better to have a forester work as your agent.

Logging contractors come in many different configurations: some are large companies with huge investments in mechanized equipment like feller-bunchers, delimbers, and slashers; others are sole proprietors, hand cutting with chainsaws and getting logs to the landing with cable skidders, bulldozers, tractors, or horses.

Logging is physical, dangerous work in a very dynamic natural environment. The forces and variables at work—among them, weather and stand conditions—provide challenges with every tree that's cut. Skilled loggers work productively, safely, and conscientiously, and the quality of their work has tremendous influence over the future growing conditions of the forest they leave behind. Highly skilled loggers are always in high demand, and most foresters have a small cadre of loggers they work with regularly. ⊙

frustrating—not to mention harmful to your land—to try to make it produce something that doesn't come naturally. To state the obvious, you need sugar maples to have a sugarbush and you need softwoods to have a deeryard. No matter how much effort you put into it, you will not be able to transform your thick hemlock stand into a sugarbush, nor will your mature stand of maples ever serve to shelter deer from harsh winter conditions. There are countless other less obvious ways in which you could try to push your forest in a direction it can't readily go.

The good news is that every piece of land has the potential to be endlessly rewarding. You will be faced with—maybe even blessed with—a set of conditions on your land that suggest certain possibilities for the land. Sometimes it takes a lot of work in the woods to transform it into something closer to what you want. And sometimes just an adjustment of expec-

tations on the part of the landowner will bring it all to fruition.

FOREST DESCRIPTION

When you're ready to start managing your forest, you should hire a forester to produce a management plan for the property. (See the sidebar on the facing page, *Finding a Forester*.) There are four major parts in a management plan: a description of the forest as it is now, a map, a plan for future activities, and a list of your goals and objectives.

First things first. We need to know what we have before we can make decisions about its future, so we'll hold off on the action plan and the goals and objectives until later. The critical first step in any plan is a clear description and inventory of the forest. The level of detail may vary, but it's considerably more than the woodland exam. A description of the

finding a forester

*I*n most states, a service forester works with landowners in each county. Employed either by the state university's extension service or by the state forestry department, these foresters are the introduction to forestry for many landowners.

One of the services they provide is to help you find a private consulting forester. They maintain a list of consulting foresters for hire in the county.

When you have some names, make some calls. Get a sense of the forester's working style and areas of expertise. The age of specialization has come to forestry, and not all foresters know the same things: some are particularly good at habitat improvement; some specialize in managing sugarbushes; others focus on growing timber. Some welcome landowner participation in the process; others feel that slows them down and would prefer to work solo.

If one sounds like a good match, make an appointment to get together. Most (not all) foresters will go for a woods walk free of charge.

Ask any potential forester for references. Get the names of three people the consultant has worked for in the last year. Talk to those landowners and ask if you can visit their woods. Make sure you can see woods that have been harvested in the last three or four years.

Go for the walk. Look around. You can get some sense of the forester's work by the quality of the trees left behind. Are the trees healthy and straight or do they look like corkscrews? And while you may not be capable of evaluating the silviculture, you can get a sense of how careful the work was. Would you want your woods to look like this?

Choose your forester well, because the slow, long-term growth of the forest means that your relationship with the forester is for the long term. You need to be comfortable with him or her. ⊙

forest should include information about the regional context of the property, inventory data, a map of the forest, and observations about the characteristics and capabilities of the land.

No property exists in isolation. It is located in a landscape and a legal jurisdiction, and it is adjacent to other land (or water). It also has a history of use that may or may not be similar to that of adjacent properties. The context of what is beyond the property boundaries might limit or expand what you can achieve inside your boundaries. If, for example, your property is bounded on one side by an interstate highway, that will limit the kinds of animals that might use your property. It also might mean that the noise level precludes constructing the getaway cabin in what might otherwise be back woods.

Consider the context of a 90-acre woodland that is situated like an island in the middle of a town dominated by cultivated cropland. A parcel the same size in

Figure 3.1 *a)* A forest surrounded by agricultural land will have substantially different plant and animal communities than *b)* one that is surrounded by more forest.
Images by Brian Hall at Harvard Forest.

the midst of 50,000 acres of forest would be entirely different in its possibilities and limitations. Driving around your area or even hiking around can provide a simple view of the regional context, but there's nothing like a bird's-eye view from an airplane or a satellite. With the availability of satellite imagery, orthophotography, and online maps and aerial photos, it is easier to get a feel for some of the ways in which a particular property fits into the larger landscape. You'll have an immediate sense of whether your land is a continuation of a large trend or whether it holds some anomalies.

TIMBER CRUISE

To evaluate a property, foresters gather several types of information, some of which are available without even visiting the property. Most counties in the Northeast have conducted soil surveys and published them in book form and/ or online, providing data about fertility,

hydrology, and engineering properties of soils. This information is available to anyone who seeks it, but foresters will have this information at their fingertips. Bedrock maps also provide important information about soil characteristics.

Soil and bedrock maps give a forester an idea of what the land might be capable of growing. Deep soils on a kind of bedrock that readily gives up its nutrients show good potential. Or you may have thin soils on granite bedrock, which offers less than ideal growing conditions.

In the forestry version of the nature versus nurture debate, nurture has equal billing, so the forester's next step is to visit the forest to see what's been nurtured there. Has the forest been given the opportunity to show its potential or has it been poorly used? This becomes more than a qualitative judgment as the forester makes quantitative measurements of what's in the forest. The way it's done is through a timber cruise, a statistical sampling of the property to estimate the vol-

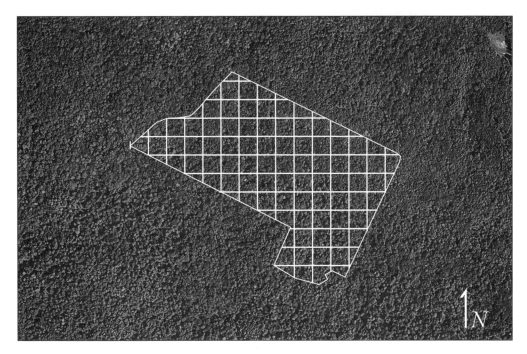

Figure 3.2   The forester cruising this forest will collect data at the intersections on the grid.

ume of timber growing on the land. The cruise also provides the forester with all sorts of additional information—including the presence of stone walls and cellar holes, wetlands, existing woods roads, boulder fields, steep slopes—that will be drawn on the map because they can affect the management of the parcel.

To come up with a tally of the volume of timber on a woodland of 1 acre or less, it would be perfectly reasonable to measure every tree that has a diameter of 4 inches or more. But that's impossible on larger lots, which is why foresters have developed ways of estimating the total volume by measuring it on a smaller percentage of the land. It often involves

setting up a series of plot points on a grid superimposed on a rough map of the property. Then, with compass and/or GPS unit in hand, the forester travels to each plot point and takes measurements. The forester enters onto a printed tally sheet or a hand-held computer the diameter and merchantable height, by species, of each tree within a prescribed distance. Sometimes, it's all trees within a fixed radius; $\frac{1}{5}$ of an acre would have a radius of 52.7 feet. More often, it's a variable radius, as the forester uses an ingenious prism that takes into account both distance and diameter of the trees. In either case, the forester then uses the data from each of the sample points to calculate the

using a prism

A prism is a deceptively simple slim wedge of glass. Here's how to use it.

Select a point on the ground and scuff it up. Hold the prism over your mark, close one eye and move clockwise in a circle, looking through the prism at each trunk at breast height. Look just over the glass at the trunk. Then look at the trunk through the glass. If you can see any part of the trunk through the glass within the outline of the trunk, it's a "count tree," which means you count it. If the prism view of the tree shifts the trunk outside of the trunk's outline, don't count it. If it's right on the borderline and you can't determine whether the trunk is in or out, count every other one.

Although you can't see the full acre from any one point, the prism adjusts the view so that each count tree represents 10 square feet of basal area per acre, which is why this one is called a 10-factor prism. If 12 trees register, for instance, that represents 120 square feet of basal area. The process is repeated at specific plot points, and the average gives you the basal area for the stand. ⊙

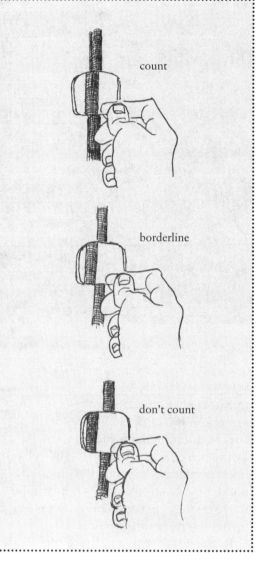

count

borderline

don't count

volume per acre in the larger stand. Before deciding how many plot points to include in the cruise, the forester takes into consideration the property's size and the heterogeneity of the forest; the more uniform it is, the fewer plot points necessary to produce accurate estimates.

Back in the office, the forester will extrapolate the data from the plot points to develop a thorough and scientifically sound inventory of the trees in the woods. This inventory provides detailed informa-

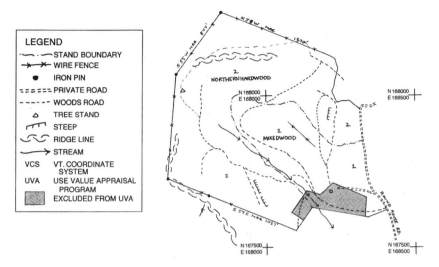

Figure 3.3   This forest has been mapped into two separate stands. Stand 1 is mixedwoods, and stand 2 is northern hardwoods.

tion that includes basal area, stems per acre, and volumes of sawlogs and pulpwood. These data are crucial in developing a plan for harvesting. (Note that explanations of all these forestry terms and others are included in the glossary. It's not necessary to understand all these concepts at this point, but you may find it helpful to refer to the glossary.)

FOREST MAP

In addition to providing the inventory data, the cruise provides a systematic and thorough view of the property that allows the forester to map the forest. As for the map, instead of naming streets or tourist attractions, a forest map primarily defines the stands. In forestry terms, a stand is an area of forest within which the conditions are similar enough that it can be covered by a single description.

Think of mapping your vegetable garden; the labels on the map would be tomatoes, cucumbers, and the like. You probably wouldn't include witchgrass, purslane, and creeping Charlie in your garden map even if they are as common in yours as they are in mine. Instead, you would choose the defining characteristic: tomato, cabbage, lettuce. Stands in a forest are less regular and less clearly defined than a garden's plants, but they can be discerned by noting the uniformity of a number of characteristics, most notably forest type.

The terms "stand" and "forest type" are sometimes used interchangeably, but they are different. Every region has recognizable species associations that repeat across the landscape. Some of the most common forest types in the Northeast are northern hardwoods (a grouping of sugar maple, beech, and yellow birch, along with several less-frequent associates), oak–pine,

natural communities

In mapping stands, foresters in the Northeast traditionally have delineated them using forest types such as these:

- spruce–fir
- northern hardwoods
- hemlock–hardwoods
- transition hardwoods
- central hardwoods
- mixedwood
- white pine
- hemlock
- pitch pine–oak
- aspen–birch
- swamp hardwood

Natural heritage programs in each state have led the way in developing typing systems that have more of a botanical and ecological focus. Widely used, they define landscapes in terms of natural communities, noting that plants and animals live within an environmental context that includes landforms and bedrock. The natural community designation describes the assemblage of plants that occupied the site in pre-settlement times.

The examples of natural communities exceed the forest types. For instance, the most common forest type in the Northeast is northern hardwoods, known by its main component species: sugar maple, beech, yellow birch. But this is not a monolithic, homogeneous grouping. As outlined in *Wetland, Woodland, Wildland: A Guide to the Natural Communities of Vermont*, northern hardwoods have at least four variants:

- beech–red maple–hemlock northern hardwood forest
- sugar maple–white ash–jack-in-the-pulpit northern hardwood forest
- yellow birch–northern hardwood forest
- white pine–northern hardwood forest

And there are five related communities:

- rich northern hardwood forest
- hemlock–northern hardwood forest
- mesic red oak–hardwood (*mesic* means having adequate moisture)
- northern hardwood talus woodland (*talus* refers to the sloping mass of rocks at the base of a cliff)
- mesic maple–ash–hickory forest

Pinpointing the natural community brings a greater degree of specificity to a description, which can be valuable. There's quite a difference between a rich northern hardwood forest and a beech–red maple–hemlock northern hardwood forest.

Foresters traditionally have used site index, a comparative measurement of a site's potential, to quantify the difference (there's more on site index in Chapter 6). Natural community classification provides a common language for foresters and ecologists to use in their discussions of forest sites. ⊙

spruce–fir, and hemlock–hardwoods. These forest types would help delineate the stands, along with other characteristics, such as age, density, and condition. If a mature, full-canopy northern hardwood stand was adjacent to a section where the same species dominated but the trees were only 4 to 6 inches in diameter, they would be mapped as different stands. One would be mature northern hardwoods, the other pole-sized northern hardwoods. Same forest type, but different age.

DESCRIPTIVE SUMMARY

To augment the inventory data and the forest map, the forester will also produce a descriptive summary of each stand's condition. This is largely an evaluation of what has happened on the land over the years. The description will answer questions like these:

- What is the land use history?
- Was it pasture or cropland?
- Are there any cultural or historical artifacts? If so, they will need protection.
- Were the trees planted?
- Did they sprout from cut stumps?
- Was it logged? Recently or long ago?
- If so, were certain species favored or discriminated against? Does good growing stock remain?
- If it was logged within the last few decades, were lots of the remaining trees wounded during logging?
- How much rot is immediately evident when you walk through the stand?
- How vigorous are the crowns of the trees?
- Is there any history of fire? Windstorm?

- What infrastructure is in place? Any roads and landings?
- Are there any hazards that restrict a logger's ability to operate?
- Is any insect or disease damage present, and is it above or below normal levels?
- Are invasive species such as buckthorn, barberry, or non-native honeysuckle present? If so, how severe is the problem?

The history of a stand partially explains its current condition; so, too, do the characteristics and capabilities of the land. Again, it's a balance between nurture and nature.

As noted above, the potential for timber production has traditionally been a primary focus of the timber cruise, so a forester will evaluate the potential for volume and value growth, given the current condition. Growth rate, vigor, and the commercial aspects of stem quality will factor into the evaluation.

The forester may report that a particular stand has little or no potential for improvement or growth in value. He may recommend that it be regenerated, which means that it's time to start over in that stand. That would be a fairly easy decision to make if the sole focus of owning the land was financial return from timber sales; if the ground is being occupied by trees that are not going to increase in value, the wise decision would be to prepare the conditions for a new stand of trees that can grow and thrive. If, however, the landowner is just as interested in the forest's capacity to provide habitat for wildlife, the value of that stand might be assessed differently.

WILDLIFE HABITAT

Because many landowners are interested primarily in the wildlife on the land, foresters have been paying increasing attention to the woodland's potential for wildlife habitat.

Maybe your forester has enough of a background in wildlife habitat to conduct a nature cruise. If not, you can find forest ecologists or wildlife consultants who can add this layer to your management plan. Or if you have the time, the inclination, and some basic training, you could take this project on yourself. By doing so, you will become more intimately connected to your land.

Animals require water, food, and cover. Different animals require different configurations of these three essential elements. If the key to good wildlife habitat were to be summed up most succinctly, it would be

Figure 3.4 a) This forest's sparse understory provides little cover for those animals that need a dense shrub layer. Contrast it with *b)* where the tangle provides ideal conditions for animals that use the ground and shrub layer.

in one word: variety. What parts of the habitat mix do your woods provide? What variety do they add to the larger landscape?

Thanks to the work of upthrust mountains and the recurrence of glaciers, the Northeast's terrain is inherently diverse. If you've ever seen a three-dimensional relief map of the Northeast, you know how little flat ground there is. Augmenting the landform diversity is the variety in land use history that results from parcels changing hands at different times and being used in different ways. Those differences in land use are evening out, however, particularly in the southern part of the region, where much of the rural land is owned by people with urban or suburban backgrounds who choose not to manage their woodland, so the forest is drifting toward more homogeneous maturity. The diversity in these forests is then due almost exclusively to any effects of natural disturbances such as ice storms or high winds.

One of the consequences of that societal preference for letting nature take its course is that the forest can be markedly lacking in an understory, an unfortunate situation because the shrub layer provides food and cover for so many species. And even though a sparse understory can occur naturally, this condition is often exacerbated by owners who tidy up their forests as they would their backyard.

The opposite is true in large sections of the industrial forest in the North Country of Maine, New Hampshire, and Vermont. These tend to be dominated by young forests marked by thickets, which develop whenever enough open space becomes available. In those areas, the challenge can be to find the mature stands that are so common to the south. Older forests south and younger forests north is a gross generality, but within those larger trends, the anomalies have particular value. Maybe your land provides it.

Diversity should be considered on at least two different scales. You'll want to first look at an aerial photo that shows just your land and its immediate surroundings; the second should be a wider view that encompasses an area 10 times the size of your land. If you own 50 acres, then take a look at topographical maps and aerial photos that cover at least 500 acres.

Start with the big picture. This broad view helps you to determine whether your land is typical of what surrounds it, or whether it may provide some unique features. As you look at the big picture, it's variety that you are seeking: variety in elevation, in land cover, in forest type. Look for streams, ponds, or wetlands, important not only for their water but also because interruptions in an overall forest cover are significant to animals. If, for instance, your reverting pastureland is the only open land in the area, it can have tremendous significance for many grassland birds, including the bobolink and eastern meadowlark, so you might decide to keep it open by brush hogging it once a year in the late summer. If, on the other hand, your land is part of an unbroken stretch of sidehill hardwoods or bottomland spruce-fir, then your challenge—if you choose to accept it—will be to introduce some variety through your management choices.

Next, focus in on the aerial photo of your own land. If a forester already has developed a forest map of your property, photocopy it and add details to it as you discover more about your land. Examine it in the same way, looking for variety in topography, in forest type, and in other landscape features.

Once you've gotten acquainted with the bird's-eye view and you can see whether your land provides any variety on the landscape scale, it's time to take a walk so you can see what it all looks like from the ground.

A NATURE CRUISE

A walk around your property's perimeter can be an informative first part of a habitat exploration because different ownerships generally mean different land use history. The habitat likely is different on the other side of the property line. I recommend an annual perimeter walk for the peace of mind of knowing that nobody has entered your land and stolen timber. Timber theft has become a significant problem in parts of the region, particularly for absentee landowners.

Earlier, I described how a forester conducts a timber cruise. In order to do a nature cruise, you need to emulate the forester. No, you don't have to set up a grid of plot points for the exploration of your woods, but you should adopt the spirit of the forester's timber cruise, if not its rigor. Cover the ground systematically. Above all, get off the trail. Bring your compass and, if you need to, your GPS unit. Explore areas you might normally bypass. If you do, it's guaranteed that you will see your land with new perspective.

WHAT ARE YOU LOOKING FOR?

On your first pass through, be sure to get the general impressions. Observe in three dimensions what you will have already seen on your topographical map and your aerial photos. See how the non-forest areas that showed up in the photos make the transition to the adjacent forest. Try to develop an eye for the stands by noticing the size of the trees and their density. Note when the forest changes in appearance. It can change in type or it can change in the size and relative density of the trees. Thus, you could find yourself going from a mature sawtimber stand of northern hardwoods into a stand of pole-sized aspen and paper birch and then (maybe slowly, maybe abruptly) into a mature stand of white pine. The transitions may be abrupt or slow because stand boundaries can be sharp or blurry. Take along a field guide if you need help identifying tree species.

Make notes as you cruise. Of course, note any of the animal species that are present. In winter, migratory birds will be gone and reptiles and amphibians and some mammals will be hibernating, but you'll be able to see the tracks of many other mammals and nonmigratory birds like grouse, turkey, and chickadees. May and June are the best months for hearing and seeing songbirds because both migrants and resident breeding birds can be found. As you cruise, make sure that you visit any of the anomalies you identified with the photos.

One of the more subtle features that you'll be looking for on your walks is

a)

b)

Figure 3.5   a) Note the complex vertical layers in this forest. It takes time to develop rich vertical diversity. *b)* Picture yourself walking through this forest. At ground level, you'll notice the horizontal diversity as you move in and out of open woods and thickets.

horizontal and vertical diversity. Think back to the discussion of forest structure in Chapter 2. Complex three-dimensionality is at the heart of habitat. And the more complex the structure of the forest, the greater number of animals whose needs will be filled there. As you take your nature cruise, make particular note of vertical diversity. Different animals use different layers of the forest. Full-canopy forests with bare park-like understories might look nice on a calendar, but they are relatively barren for wildlife. Shrub layers and trees half the height of the can-

opy add three-dimensional complexity.

Finally, as you walk through your woods, use the following checklist and make note of special features, ranging from landscape scale to individual trees, that are a boon to many species of wildlife. Add these features to your map.

Wetlands. Swamps, marshes, bogs. How do you tell the difference between them? Seasonally wet, a swamp is a wetland with trees growing in it. Adjacent to a lake or other water body, a marsh has water flowing through it and features grasses and sedges, including the cattail. A bog is wet all year though it has no inflow or outflow. Its vegetation consists largely of acid-loving dwarf shrubs and sphagnum moss. Wetlands are home to a tremendous variety of plants and animals. Animals are drawn by water, thick cover, and food, including invertebrates and plants unique to wetlands.

Vernal pools. These are specialized wetlands—depressions in the forest floor that hold water only in spring. They have no inlets or outlets. Void of living vegetation, they might contain some fallen woody debris. They are important habitat for a number of species of salamanders, frogs, and invertebrates such as fairy shrimp, which can only reproduce successfully because vernal pools have no fish.

Lakes, ponds. Shorelines have some of the same qualities as riparian zones. They also provide nesting sites for waterfowl. If the lake is large enough, it might have loons.

Rivers or streams. Not only the watercourse is important; so is the vegetation at the edge of rivers and streams. Known

Figure 3.6 *a)* The dead beech tree is home to many decomposers and to those that feed on them; *b)* a vernal pool in early spring; *c)* a pileated woodpecker excavated the holes in this dead tree, searching for carpenter ants.

as the riparian zone, the margin of a river or stream serves as a travel corridor for many species.

Beaver ponds. These are true magnets for wildlife ranging from moose to muskrat. Waterfowl, songbirds, reptiles and amphibians, herons, otter, mink—all are drawn to the cover and food the beaver's pond creates.

Woodland seeps or springs. Particularly important for salamanders, they are also sought out by turkeys, bears, and migrating birds in the spring. The surrounding ground is the first to thaw, and seep vegetation is the first to green up in the spring.

Dead and down wood. Decomposing trunks, limbs, and stumps are used by many species of reptiles, amphibians, birds, and mammals. They provide cover, moisture, nest and den sites, and food in the form of insects and other invertebrates, tiny organisms, and fungi. This is an important and easily overlooked habitat feature.

Stone walls or cellar holes. Besides being remnants of our past, these can provide safe openings for ground-dwelling animals like snakes and burrowing mammals, and hiding places for chipmunks and mice.

Groves of beech or oak. The seeds of all trees provide food. Beechnuts and acorns are a critical source of protein, fat, and vitamins for animals preparing for winter. Before entering hibernation, bears load up on beechnuts if they are available. When they climb a beech in pursuit of nuts, bears leave claw marks on the tree's smooth bark that will show up for years. They gorge on acorns, too, as do deer, who also need to put on fat to get through the winter. Beechnuts and acorns, known as hard mast, are also eaten by turkeys.

Soft mast. Many trees and shrubs provide fruits and berries, and hundreds of species rely on them. Particularly important are cherries (from the black cherry to the pin cherry), blackberries, raspberries, and wild apples. Wild apples are a particularly important late-season food. In your woods, note the presence of apple trees, either as single trees or—if you and the wildlife are even luckier—old orchards. Other trees, such as hophornbeam, have persistent catkins that provide food for many months.

Overstory inclusions. A few softwoods within a predominately hardwood stand provide cover and nesting sites for birds. Hardwoods within softwood stands provide food. Both provide structural diversity.

Large cavity trees. Woodpeckers are the excavators, but the cavities they make are used in subsequent years as nest sites by many birds and as den sites for mammals. Songbirds, squirrels, bats, weasels, owls, and raccoons are among the many species that use cavities for nesting. As the crown dies back, dead trees are used as perches and roosts. When looking for cavity trees, think also of those in the future. Prime candidates are injured trees and those with a limb broken off. Think also of leaving large trees in your woodlot, those that are too poorly formed to be a sawlog and too big to be handled as firewood.

Cliffs and ledges. Important niches for bobcats, which have had much of their habitat usurped by coyotes.

Raptor nests. Hawks and owls nest high in the canopy, making their own nests or re-using other species' nests of twigs and sticks. Many nests are used year after year, especially if there is minimal human activity near the nests during breeding season.

Deer wintering areas. In winter, deer herd up in stands of softwood for protection from the harsh conditions. One sign that deer are using an area in winter is overbrowsed hardwood saplings (thick branching makes them look broomy) within primarily softwood stands. Deer are such efficient generalists that they can find food and cover almost anywhere nine months of the year. Winter habitat is the only limiting factor; without it, many deer will die during prolonged periods of deep snow and below zero temperatures.

Rare plant or animal sites or communities. You'll probably need outside help to confirm these features, but your legwork can get the process started. If an area looks substantially different from its surroundings, take note of the species of plants. Check with your state natural heritage office (most likely within the fish and wildlife department) or with The Nature Conservancy to see whether any rare sites are mapped on your land. Depending on the state, these sites vary widely, from floodplain forests to white cedar swamps to natural stands of red pine. ◙

CHAPTER 4

PRODUCTS FROM THE FOREST

Forest products are, quite simply, the things we obtain from the forest. Traditionally, we've used that term for wood or maple syrup or Christmas trees—physical objects whose sale puts money into the pocket of the landowner or producer. Many items fit this description, and we're going to discuss them later in this chapter, but the most important forest product of all is the fully functioning forest system itself.

How can a forest be a product?

Here's the dictionary definition of product: "Something produced by human or mechanical effort or by a natural process." That's pretty straightforward: the essence is that a product comes about as the result of a process. A forest, as described in Chapter 2, contains countless organisms interacting through various natural processes on a particular piece of ground. When those processes are proceeding without interruption in a system that's self-sustaining (not to ignore the crucial input from the sun), the result is a fully functioning forest. The function can be compromised by actions that cause topsoil to disappear downhill or that damage seeps, streams, or wetlands. Worse, the forest can be converted to other uses. Agricultural conversion, as we saw, can be temporary; pavement, concrete, and steel bring about more permanent change. It can be argued that a fully functioning society needs these additions for the sake of a vibrant economy, but enlightened land use planning adds onto existing infrastructure and takes into consideration the societal benefits that natural systems provide.

None of the dictionary definitions of product say anything explicitly about usefulness or value. Regardless, I would suggest that implicit in our understanding of a product is that it is of use to us, either in its original natural form or when it is transformed into something else. Because it has usefulness, it has value and can be sold. More than likely, that accurately describes the forestland you own, the 13 or 76 or 894 acres that mean a lot to you. It has usefulness and value to you, and the ownership of it will someday be sold or given to someone else.

In earlier chapters, we began to paint a picture of what makes forestland so important. It's a valuable product, not only to its owners but also to the public at large because of the tremendous services it provides. The forest cleanses water and air, provides habitat for wildlife, and mitigates the effects of climate change. Collectively, forest landowners provide these beneficial services for the society as a whole, but they are not yet compensated directly for doing so. That may change in the future. While the importance of any given woodlot can seem insignificant in the context of the Northeast's forested landscape, the cumulative effect of all of these ownerships is crucial.

Let's take a closer look at some of the functions and services of forests that make them unquantifiably valuable to the larger community.

WOODS AND WATER

Wildlife habitat is such an important ecosystem service that it's discussed in detail in other places in this book, so I will not spend time on it here. Instead, let me turn immediately to water.

In looking at a land-cover map of the Northeast, it becomes readily apparent that forests are the predominant cover type at 73 percent of the land mass. What's not immediately apparent is how much water exists in those woods. Just as the human body is said to be 98 percent water, this living, breathing forest is awash in H_2O. Within and throughout this forestland are bodies of water, from glacier-made lakes the size of Seneca, Winnipesauke, and Moosehead to small ponds made by beavers or bulldozers. The landscape is dotted with bogs, swamps, marshes, and ephemeral pools. Then there's the flowing water, ranging from major rivers like the Hudson and the Kennebec to the small step-across streams that originate in the uplands.

Forests play host to the hydrologic cycle and play an active role in it. While not classified as a temperate rainforest, most of the Northeast receives regular precipitation throughout the year in the form of either rain or snow. Forests, more particularly the forest soils, act as huge sponges, absorbing much of the rainfall and snowmelt. Then, over time, they slowly meter it out into the groundwater and surface waters, a process that sustains springs, wells, and streams through dry spells. In a parallel process called evapotranspiration, trees "exhale" tremendous volumes of moisture back into the atmosphere, which will later fall somewhere as rain, hail, sleet, or snow.

This absorption and gradual release of water also reduces the severity of flooding. The thick layer of humus—organic matter—that accumulates as the top layer of soil in older forests is particularly good at absorbing water and can hold many times its dry weight. This greatly reduces the peak flows during and immediately following heavy rains and rapid snow melt. We've recently had some catastrophic flooding in each state in the Northeast with widespread damage to roads, bridges, and buildings. Such flooding is largely a result of a steady accumulation of more and more impervious surfaces adjacent to streams and rivers that have been straightened and armored with rip-rap to meet our needs. Forests counter this effect and can play a large role in reducing flooding and the devastation to human lives and property that might otherwise occur. Without forests, the floods would be much worse than they've been.

In addition to regulating the volume of water available, forests also clean it. As precipitation percolates through foliage and forest soils, it is filtered as it contacts surface textures, which strip it of many of the pollutants that it has washed out of the atmosphere. The forest retains chemicals that could enter ground water or surface water. Some of these chemicals, such as nitrates, act as nutrients to the trees and other forest plants. Others are less benign. Sulfur compounds acidify the water, which then leaches valuable calcium and other ions from the soils. The result is lowered soil pH, making the site less hospitable to some plant species.

It would be difficult to design a more efficient self-cleaning system: the air contains pollutants so you spray water through it to bring the bad stuff to the ground; once it's on the ground, run the water through some filters, and when it comes out the other end, it's so clean you can drink it. To top it all off, the filters grow things we need and provide a beautiful place to take a walk. Remarkable.

The drinking water is not just for the wells and springs serving rural homes and towns. Many municipalities provide their citizens drinking water from wells and reservoirs surrounded by forests. In fact, the public water used by the region's two largest cities, New York and Boston, comes from such sources, and it requires little or no treatment. The water authorities can do that because the reservoirs—Quabbin in

Massachusetts and a network of them in the Catskills—are fed by water originating in forests that naturally purify the water. It's worth noting that the streams feeding these reservoirs run through land owned not only by the government but also by private landowners, and much of this private land is in active agricultural and forestry production. The land management practices in these watersheds emphasize forested buffers along even the smallest streams, which contributes to the purity of the drinking water.

Across the Northeast, these services —flood control, water absorption and metering, and water filtering—are worth untold billions of dollars each year. When forests are removed and the land is developed into malls, highways, and housing developments, these services are lost at great cost to the people and communities affected.

CLEAN, COOL, CALM AIR

Just as forests affect the water that moves through them, they also affect the air that flows over and around the trees. Collectively, the trees and other plants act as a giant filter. Particulates in the air glom onto the vegetation. Unseen pollutants, such as ozone, react with or are adsorbed onto plant surfaces and are thus removed from the air. In this way, plants are "taking one for the team" because they can be damaged by the pollutants.

The evapotranspiration and shading by trees ameliorates temperature extremes. As we noted earlier, on a hot summer day it will be noticeably cooler in a forest than in an adjacent field or in a nearby town. It's not only for a dose of natural beauty in an otherwise urban jungle that trees are planted in cities. This "natural air conditioning" in forested parks in urban settings provides escape from summer's often brutal heat. Similarly, street trees and yard trees work wonders.

Wind speed is far lower within a forest stand than it is in a field. Winter's wind chill is thus significantly reduced, making wooded areas more comfortable on cold, windy days. Many birds and mammals take advantage of this, seeking cover in dense evergreen areas when winter conditions are harsh. The evergreens also intercept much of the snowfall, so the snow depth on the ground under the trees is significantly less than under nearby deciduous trees. Recall our description of deeryards in the previous chapter. Conditions in these sheltered areas are commonly referred to as microclimates.

BEAUTY AND RECREATION

Forested countryside is beautiful—just ask your local landscape painter—and this beauty attracts many people to rural parts of the Northeast for their vacations. A backdrop of forested hills or mountains adds charm to small villages and can make cities more appealing. And an opportunity for recreation—walking, hiking, birding, skiing, hunting, and fishing—is a big part of why people vacation in rural areas.

Views have a dramatic impact on land prices. For land with a million-dollar view, its price increases manyfold, sometimes to well over $10,000 an acre, a clear measure of the value people put on beauty.

For those of us who live and work in rural areas, the views from our homes, the attractiveness of the countryside as we travel around, and the availability of recreation right out our back doors are a big part of why we live where we do. We live where other people come for vacation, and forests are a major part of the attraction.

People spend money while visiting the region for birding, hiking, hunting, and fishing, which contributes a great deal to the rural economy. Sales of clothing, equipment, food, and lodging support local businesses, while license fees paid by hunters and anglers provide much of the annual budget for state fish and game departments. Forgetting for a moment the large contributions to cash flow made by the timber industry, forests in and of themselves contribute to the financial well-being of local communities.

CARBON SEQUESTRATION

Green plants, through photosynthesis, absorb carbon dioxide from the air and chemically change it into sugars, which are necessary for·the life processes of the plant. These sugars are also the building blocks for the cellulose and lignin that make up the plant's structure. One byproduct of photosynthesis is oxygen, which is released to the atmosphere—in fact, the atmosphere would hold little free oxygen, which is essential to life on the planet, if it weren't for the continual photosynthesis of plants. Although green plants use some of that oxygen to burn sugars as part of their own metabolism, emitting carbon dioxide as they do so, the net result of plant life is an increase in oxygen and a decrease in carbon dioxide in the atmosphere.

Trees are very effective at removing carbon dioxide from the atmosphere—sequestering it, to use the adopted phrase—so maintaining a cover of trees can help reduce the effects of atmospheric carbon accumulation. Like oceans, forests are a carbon sink. Forests tie up carbon in tree trunks, limbs, twigs, and leaves and below the surface in tree roots and other organic matter in the soil.

How much carbon is tied up in forests? Are older established forests more effective carbon sinks than young, rapidly growing forests? What is it all worth to society at large? Scientists at the intersection of economics, public policy, silviculture, forest mensuration, and biochemistry are trying to come up with a viable system for measuring a forest's carbon balance sheet. That process is an early step taken by a nation reluctantly acknowledging the damaging consequences of too much carbon dioxide in the atmosphere.

We expect a lot from our forests, but it's important that we not overstate the case for their capacity as a carbon sink to solve the problem of global climate change. The current climate crisis is a byproduct of the otherwise brilliant technological achievement of extracting coal and oil long buried beneath the earth's surface and using them for fuels to heat our homes, drive our engines, and produce our electricity. Finding and using heretofore useless buried matter to fuel the industrialization and the modernization of our world can't help but be

viewed as an incredible accomplishment, and it has made many people, corporations, and nations very wealthy. Unfortunately, the byproduct of that accomplishment is that we have skewed a delicate balance maintained over the eons as global temperatures rose and fell. Whereas all that carbon was once sitting benignly in the ground, having been processed and stored there for millions of years, much of it is now suddenly present in an altered form in the air above us. Below us, it was part of a natural process; above us, it's a heat-deflecting ceiling.

The magnitude of the problem of global climate change dwarfs what forests can reasonably be counted on to do. Public policy decisions, rather than a free market in carbon credits, will likely have the largest impact on how landowners are compensated for sequestering carbon in their forests. It would be unfortunate, however, if the payment for multi-generation storage of carbon inadvertently kept landowners from participating in established or new markets for the many tangible products our forests provide.

One of the beauties of the way the forest works is that we can make prudent withdrawals of some products without compromising the whole or diminishing the prospects for other compatible products. I'll go into depth on this in Chapter 6, but in essence, we can remove a load of logs without disturbing the patch of shade-loving ginseng or compromising the habitat for black-throated blue warblers. On the other hand, committing a forest to a non-harvest regime for 99 years in exchange for an annual per-acre payment for carbon sequestration precludes most, if not all, other options. For someone trying to find other sources of revenue to offset real costs of ownership, making this type of commitment might not be prudent and will surely decrease timber productivity and value.

There are two ways to reduce carbon concentration in the atmosphere: dramatic reductions in our overall energy consumption, and development of a mix of renewable sources of energy so we can cease pumping carbon from beneath the earth's crust into the atmosphere. One of the sources that could be a significant part of the future energy mix is biomass from wood; thus forests can have another role in combating climate change.

These services provided by the forest are not what most people immediately think of when forest products come to mind. Let's move on to our discussion of the more traditional forest products—those made from trees—and we won't start with biomass but at the other end of the value spectrum: veneer.

VENEER

A tree's economic value comes from its usefulness as the raw material for a product. The more valuable the product that can come from it, the more valuable the tree. In the last few decades, the most valuable product from a tree has been veneer, the thin sheet of wood used as the outside skin on furniture, paneling, and other laminated surfaces. It shows its pretty face while hiding the composite board or other inexpensive material that is glued beneath.

Only a remarkable tree can produce veneer-grade wood, so let me describe the perfect tree. In the Northeast, it is a hardwood, preferably black cherry, sugar maple, or red oak, though fashions and values do shift, and yellow birch and white ash are strong runners-up. The tree has a large diameter and is growing straight and tall, at least 30 to 40 feet before it branches out and forms a crown. The crown accounts for one-third of the tree's overall height, and the tree is full even though it might not have the lollypop shape we all drew as kids. To have achieved this perfect form, the tree has competed with cohorts all along the way, from sapling to pole to small sawtimber to large sawtimber. It excelled at using the sun, water, and soil nutrients to establish a full, dominant crown and add inches in diameter. It escaped injury from logging and from falling trees and other natural disturbances.

This tree is so valuable because its lowest 8-foot log (and since we're describing perfection, the next highest, too) is gun-barrel straight. A perfect veneer log, if there were such a thing, would be a true cylinder. And inside that perfect log, all the growth rings would be the same distance apart, and the wood would be uniform, with no blemishes and no discolorations. But perfection doesn't come easily, compromised as it is by the nature of how trees grow.

Big trees start out as saplings with branches forming from the center stem. Both stem and branch grow in length and girth. If the lower branches fall off early (as they do when the trees start out packed closely together and little light reaches the lower part of the tree), the branch stubs will be covered over with many layers of new wood, one layer for each year the tree's girth expands. When the mature tree is cut and its logs are sawn, sliced, or peeled, the remnants of those branches show up as knots. Logs cut from trees that have grown many inches of clear wood over those branch stubs (enough wood that the stubs no longer show in the bark) are the veneer buyer's version of the Holy Grail.

A perfect cylindrical shape is not physically possible for a tree. Instead, the trunks of all trees are shaped like cones, because each year they add a layer of wood onto existing wood, and the higher you go in a

tree, the fewer years of growth there have been. Taper is a given; it can't be avoided. The less taper a tree has—the closer it is to a cylinder—the more valuable it is. In general, veneer brings the highest price for any log, hardwood or softwood, though the premium in the softwood species is much less dramatic.

Veneer logs are cut into thin sheets of wood, and most veneer is laminated into products such as plywood and linear veneer lumber, though some is used in a single layer for things like popsicle sticks, tongue depressors, and bushel baskets. There are two different approaches to making these thin sheets. Rotary veneer is made by spinning the log on a lathe,

Figure 4.1   a) This forest-grown sugar maple has perfect form and would provide a veneer log; *b)* this maple's prominent branch stubs show that it grew in the open for many years. It will have large knots that make it useless for lumber.

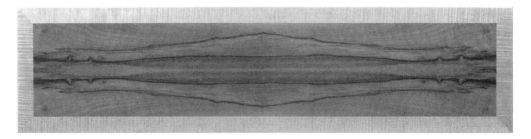

Figure 4.2 Slicer veneer allows furniture makers to position grain patterns in striking ways, as in this table top. *Photo courtesy of Rees Tulloss.*

while a knife longer than the length of the log peels off a continuous layer of veneer. If you were to mount a roll of paper towels on a rack and unroll its entire length, you would be approximating rotary veneer production. At a certain point, the log is reduced to the branchy, knotty core surrounding the pith—the spongy vessel at the innermost of the tree's concentric circles—which is not valuable.

Slicer processing is used for the more valuable veneer. In this process, the log is sliced lengthwise over and over. Instead of a single continuous sheet, the output is a stack of many slices. The two methods result in different grain patterns in the veneer, with the slicer process much more flexible in its output. In applications of slicer veneer, grain patterns can be repeated to very nice effect. Unless constructed solely of solid wood, the faces of fine furniture and paneling are made with slicer veneer. The rotary process is faster and less costly, and it can produce high-grade veneer, but it's the method for making construction-grade plywood and other industrial products.

Log buyers who want to produce appearance-grade veneer are fussy, paying top dollar only for logs that are straight and round, and have their pith exactly in the center. Most veneer logs are knot-free, though in white pine, small red knots can be desirable. The log's color and ratio of heartwood to sapwood are often important. In sugar maple, for instance, heartwood must account for less than one-third the diameter because it's the creamy white sapwood that's so valuable. It's the opposite with black cherry, where the heartwood is the prize. Some factors that don't come into play with sawlogs are of critical importance in the best veneer logs: you want uniformity of growth rate but don't want flaws such as mineral stain, pitch pockets, and worm track.

If the veneer logs are to be used for structural plywood, rather than appearance-grade veneer, their characteristics overlap with those of sawlogs.

SAWLOGS

If a tree doesn't contain a veneer log, the next best product is a sawlog. These are relatively straight logs that will be sawn into lumber, timbers, or other solid products. Most sawmills specialize in certain species and kinds of lumber, so they purchase logs suitable for their machinery and products.

Lumber has many uses, and each has different criteria for what is suitable. For some uses, strength is the most important consideration; for others, it's appearance. Some products are commodities (for instance, 2 x 4s for construction), whereas others are specialty products, such as clear, knot-free hardwood lumber for high-end furniture.

Most logs in the Northeast are cut to specific lengths before they are sold to sawmills. (In some regions, it is more common to sell logs tree-length, and the stems are cut to length at the sawmill.) For softwood trees, common log lengths are 8 to 16 feet, with 2-foot increments. For hardwoods, the same range of lengths applies, though it's common to sell logs in 1-foot increments. Sawmills require (as do veneer mills) that every sawlog has a trim allowance, which is 4 to 6 inches of extra length so that boards sawn from the log can be trimmed to their nominal length. A 9-foot hardwood log has to be 9'6". If it is 9'2", it will be scaled at the next shorter acceptable length, in this case, as an 8-foot log.

Mills sawing softwoods generally prefer to saw longer logs because it takes about the same amount of time to handle and saw a short log as it does a long one. Therefore, many softwood mills pay more for long logs than for short logs and may refuse to accept 8- and 10-foot logs, or accept only a few short logs per truckload.

Typical minimum log diameters (measured at the small end) in the Northeast are 5 or 6 inches for spruce and fir (spruce and fir tend to grow very straight and are typically sawn into construction material such as 2 x 4s on high-speed, automated machinery), 8 inches for white pine, 8 inches for hardwood pallet logs, and 10 inches for the higher grades of hardwoods. Hardwood log value increases dramatically as the diameter increases. In combination with knot size and log length, log diameters determine log grades, with larger diameter logs usually giving higher production rates and yielding more valuable products.

The size and characteristics of knots are an important factor in both the strength and appearance of a piece of softwood lumber. Therefore mills grade logs based on the maximum allowable size of knots and whether the knots are red or black. (See sidebar, *Knotty or Nice?*, on page 66 for an explanation of this distinction.)

Hardwood logs are sawn into products where strength is important (pallets, railroad ties, and structural material) and where appearance is important (furniture, cabinets, and flooring). Often both types of products are sawn from the same log; for instance, the outer boards of an oak log may be used for furniture parts while the center of the log may be used for making a railroad tie or pallets.

Where strength is crucial, the key factors are knot size (smaller is better), straightness of grain, and soundness (lack of decay, cracks, and splits). Where appearance counts, mills are trying to produce lumber that can be cut into adequately sized pieces without knots and other "defects" (holes, cracks, splits, and color stain).

knotty or nice?

*R*ed knots are okay; black knots are unacceptable. Why would color matter so much?

The difference between a red knot and a black knot goes beyond color. The distinction lies in whether the source of the knot, a branch, was alive when the tree was cut. Lower branches that don't get sunlight often die but stay attached to the tree, creating a junction of dead branch and live tree.

The tree grows, but the dead branch doesn't, and there's a tenuous bond between the two. This becomes a problem in lumber because the knot is not intergrown with the surrounding wood, so it can come loose and fall out of the board. This is known as a black knot.

The dead wood is black, as opposed to a red knot, whose source branch was alive when the tree was harvested.

Therefore, the branch and trunk were growing together, and the knot can't fall out of the board and leave a hole.

The terms apply to boards as well as logs, and the type of knots and their diameters relative to board or timber width are grading criteria for softwood lumber and timbers. Note that for logs with black knots, the branch was alive earlier in the tree's life and thus boards cut from the interior of the log will likely have red knots rather than black knots. That said, it's the outside of the tree that provides the best lumber.

This is a good argument for pruning sawtimber, particularly white pine, which can put on many inches of clear wood beyond the pruned branch stubs.

Few people prune hardwoods because these trees tend to self-prune if grown close to each other. There will be much more on the topic of stocking density of trees in Chapter 6.☉

a) b)

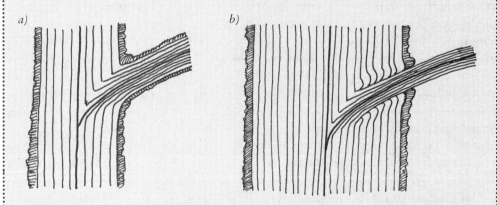

Figure 4.3 a) The tree on the left has continuous bark over the trunk and branch because the branch is still alive. Knots in lumber from it will be tight, red knots. *b)* Contrast that with the tree on the right, with a dead branch stub protruding through the bark. This will produce loose, black knots in the lumber.

Within the lumber spectrum, the most valuable product is clear lumber used to make furniture. Knots or branch stubs (the remnants of branches overgrown by the bole) are the main limiting factors, along with wounds, seams, and—in light-colored hardwoods like sugar maple where the value is in the white sapwood—too much heartwood. The larger the clear board that can be sawn from it, the more the sawmill will pay for the tree. Log graders scrutinize the surface and the cut ends, but they don't know the whole story until the log is opened up.

The prime sawlogs are large—at least 16 inches in diameter—and as free of discernible defects as possible. The highest prices are paid for logs that have four clear sides. Even though a log is round, log buyers see it with four faces, which makes sense because once the outer slabs are sawn off, what remains is four-sided. Prices drop for smaller diameters and for logs with only three clear sides. A log with two clear sides brings even less because the sawyer will get fewer valuable boards from a log with this many defects.

The next major factor in determining value is species. No matter how perfectly cylindrical your hophornbeam might be, it's not going to make a log buyer reach for his wallet. In the Northeast, the most valuable species are sugar maple, black cherry, and red oak. These three have for decades been the choice hardwoods, though fashion dictates which among them is the most highly sought: the white wood of maple, the rich tones of cherry, or the distinctive grain of oak. The next tier of value includes white ash, yellow birch,

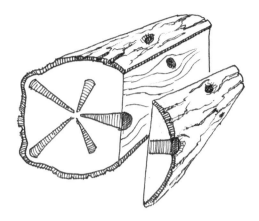

Figure 4.4   This white pine log shows one whorl at the end of the log and knots from another one midway up the log. Knots show up in the squared-off lumber whether or not they are visible in the bark.

and paper birch. Despite fluctuations in the demand for any of these six species, it's a safe bet that as long as there is a lumber industry, there's always going to be a demand for the high-end hardwoods.

The one softwood that can be added to the list of desirable species is white pine. It never has as much value per board foot as the top-tier hardwoods, but it grows rapidly and puts on more board feet per acre than the hardwoods can. And the wood has long been used for flooring, paneling, and furniture.

The key to the value of these seven species is that for each of them there are several different grades, and thus prices, based on the log's form and size. As trees grow and can produce larger logs, there's the obvious growth in volume. In addition, these species graduate into higher classes of products as they grow. The jumps in grade, and thus value—based

High	Intermediate	Low
Black cherry	Red maple	American beech
Sugar maple	White oak	Eastern hemlock
Red oak	Black birch	
White ash	Spruce	Aspens
Yellow birch	Balsam fir	Tamarack
White pine	White cedar	Hickories
Paper birch		Black locust
		Red pine

Figure 4.5 Relative values of common species in the Northeast. Local markets influence the relative desirability of some species.

almost entirely on reaching the next diameter threshold—can be dramatic.

Contrast that with a spruce or hemlock log. No matter how good it is, at the mill it's a commodity, not a treasure. On the positive side, the yield (per tree and per acre) for spruce rivals pine and far exceeds the hardwoods. Spruce can grow successfully at greater density per acre, has a stronger tendency to maintain a single straight stem, grows taller, and is usable down to a 4-inch diameter (at the small end). But there is no differentiation in grade, so every board foot of spruce brings the same price. Volume per acre is more important than knot size or perceived defects. Balsam fir has characteristics similar to the three spruces (red, white, black), and the four are sold interchangeably and referred to as spruce. If the fir, however, is a significant proportion of the mix, the price paid will probably be lowered because balsam fir has more defects and takes longer to kiln dry.

In summary, veneer logs and sawlogs come from trees that have grown straight and have relatively little branching in their lower trunks. The difference between a log that goes to a veneer mill instead of a sawmill can seem slight. The gradations in quality are subtle, but highly skilled log buyers earn their keep by making such value judgments at a glance. It's truly a challenge to look at a log and, from that vantage point only, determine what the boards within it will look like. Profit margins are slim in sawmills, and log buyers who guess wrong too often—who see too much value in a load of logs—don't stay employed.

LOW-GRADE WOOD

The difference between the high-value trees and the ones that don't make the grade is black and white. It's the wheat from the chaff. Once you know what to look for, you won't confuse the two. Low-grade trees are crooked, twisted, or contorted; they have wounds or scars or seams. They keep their low limbs and fork into multiple trunks. It would be difficult to get a stable piece of lumber from these trees.

A number of things can happen to a growing tree that can compromise its form and diminish its value. While the veneer tree excelled among its cohorts, low-grade trees might have grown without competition. A tree that grows on its own, with plenty of space around it, benefits from all the sunlight and nutrients and spreads its limbs in appreciation. Great conditions for a shade tree; terrible for a lumber tree.

A variation on this occurs when a tree grows on the edge of a field or pasture. On the open side, it will develop long lower limbs reaching out for the sun, and this unbalanced existence compromises the integrity of the wood.

Saplings can split into multiple trunks within inches of the ground, making them susceptible to separating later when their weight is measured in tons and not ounces. If they don't split, the close proximity of the trunks keeps each of them from attaining roundness until farther up in the tree.

Injuries at any stage of development can cause defects. When overhead limbs or entire trees fall on adjacent trees, they can strip them of branches or scrape bark from their boles. Trees can be remarkably adept at walling off these wounds, but some wood is damaged and the results are usually apparent. And sometimes the open wound does not close up before a fungus finds the opening. This kind of damage occurs naturally, but it can also happen during a logging operation if a falling tree scrapes others on its way down.

Many woodlots in the Northeast still have trees that were bent over during the hurricane of 1938. These trees were pinned by other trees nearly parallel to the ground and then when freed from that weight, they responded to the sudden light by correcting themselves and growing straight either from the tip or from a branch pointed in the right direction. It doesn't take a hurricane, however, for that sequence of events to throw a kink into a trunk. Every forest has plenty of crooked

Figure 4.6   a) This forest-grown white pine has 40 feet of trunk before any branching. The hardwoods below it got started in a thinning 10 years ago. Compare its form to *b)* an open-grown white pine, whose branching begins three feet above the ground.

Figure 4.7 This white ash is a vigorous tree that outpaced its cohorts. Because its form is so rough, it has little commercial value, but it has great value for its seeds, its contribution to forest structure, and its ultimate future as a large dead tree—either standing or on the forest floor.

saplings and poles that are overcoming this sort of challenge to their future.

Any deviation from the straight, long trunk brings a tree into the category of low-grade. It's important to note that this value judgment is only on its capacity to provide products when cut. When standing in a forest, it could be acquitting itself very nicely in its function as a tree. It could be sequestering lots of carbon, photosynthesizing like a banshee, and playing host to a dozen birds' nests in its branches. Under certain circumstances, that's all anyone would ask of this tree. If, on the other hand, financial return from the sale of products is a management goal, this tree is taking up space that could be used by one with more potential for value. Selling it as low-grade wood makes sense if by doing so other more valuable trees can thrive.

I don't want to get ahead of myself, because we'll discuss forest management in depth in later chapters, but this sort of forest improvement is at the heart of any discussion of management. All other things being equal, growing straight, healthy trees that can provide real financial return makes more sense than growing a forest full of poorly formed trees that, when harvested, yield little or no income.

Low-grade wood has three distinct uses: pulpwood, firewood, or biomass. Among these three, there is considerable overlap, and many poorly formed hardwood trees could find themselves on a truck to any of these markets. Some areas in the Northeast have access to all three markets; others suffer from very little demand for any low-grade wood, which challenges forest managers who are trying to improve a forest's growing stock.

FIREWOOD

Around the world, ever since humans learned to make fires, wood has been used for cooking and heating. This has continued unabated for eons in some parts of the world, but for many people in the developed nations, other fuels have supplanted wood for domestic use.

In the Northeast, we use a disproportionate amount of heating oil. Of the 10 million households that use heating oil,

78 percent of them are in the Northeast. That startling number stems partly from the fact that most of the people in this largely rural area live in cities, where firewood is expensive and inconvenient. The only connection these city-dwellers have to their domestic fuel is through the meter that measures delivery and the monthly bill that results. But even in the rural areas surrounded by forests, propane and heating oil heat most houses.

Occasionally, there is a rush to firewood and wood-burning stoves. The first of these followed the oil embargo in the 1970s. The dramatic rise in oil prices brought worries about future availability of heating oil and rekindled interest in wood for heating homes. Heating engineers developed new wood stoves that burned wood more efficiently and could hold a fire overnight. Insulated metal chimneys made installing wood stoves easier and less expensive than masonry chimneys. These all contributed to a boom in sales of wood stoves and firewood.

Since then, the rise and fall of firewood use has occurred in response to broad changes in fossil fuel prices and public perceptions about the future availability of fossil fuels. When the price per gallon of heating oil seems unreasonably high, people switch to firewood. This has opened up a market for outdoor wood boilers, which have become common in the rural Northeast. Early models were notorious for filling the neighborhood with smoke, and most states have acted to regulate the manufacture of these boilers, so those sold today burn more efficiently. When today's models are used properly—hot fires, tall smokestacks—they are no more hazardous than efficient woodstoves. Many of the early models, however, are still smoldering and smoking, and their presence in the neighborhood turns many people against wood as a fuel.

This is unfortunate, because replacing fossil fuels with firewood decreases our dependence on imported energy, which most people agree is good public policy. Firewood is rarely transported long distances, so money stays in the immediate region to help sustain the local economy. And because wood is a carbon-neutral fuel, burning it doesn't contribute to climate change. Wood is our first fuel, and we may ultimately decide that it is our best fuel.

Firewood is usually sold by the cord, which is a measure of volume. A standard cord is a stack of wood, bark, and air with a volume of 128 cubic feet; the prototypical cord is a stack 4 feet high, 4 feet wide, and 8 feet long. The actual volume of wood in a cord depends on the mix of piece sizes, the bark thickness, and how closely the pieces are stacked. In some areas, the term "face cord" is used to denote a volume of firewood contained in a stack that measures 4 feet high by 8 feet long by the length of the individual pieces. The volume in a face cord therefore depends on the length of the pieces, so if the wood is cut into 16-inch lengths—a fairly typical length for woodstoves—a face cord would hold only one-third of a cord.

A pound of dry maple contains essentially the same BTUs as a pound of dry pine, but firewood is sold not by weight but by volume. Thus, a cord of high-density maple has far more BTUs available than a cord of low-density pine because

christmas trees and maple syrup

*O*ther forest products deserve to be mentioned, and two in particular catch most people's attention when they first own a piece of land: Christmas trees and maple syrup.

CHRISTMAS TREES

Christmas trees are a cash crop for thousands of growers in the Northeast. Grown in plantations, Christmas trees make good use of reverting pasture or cropland, especially if the land has well-drained soils and suitable aspect. Growers who devote the time to cultivating the trees can make nice supplemental income.

Fraser fir and balsam fir tend to be the most popular trees, though some people swear by a balsam variety called Canaan. Planted on a 6-foot by 6-foot grid, you can grow 1,210 trees per acre, but roads will take some of that space and some trees will die along the way (figure loss of 5 to 10 percent). A Christmas tree grows from seedling to finished 7-foot tree in 9 to 12 years, which can be reduced if you start with older, heartier transplants. Sell all those trees at $35 each, and that's nice money.

Sales revenue, however, doesn't just appear in the mailbox on Christmas Eve. Many gung-ho new growers underestimate how much work it entails, and you don't need to drive too far to come across a conifer forest that has

Figure 4.8 *a)* A small Christmas tree plantation can be a good use for unused pasture. *Photo courtesy of Elysian Hills Tree Farm.* *b)* This plantation of balsam firs was started long ago with Christmas trees in mind, but it didn't quite pan out. *Photo by Dave Mance III.*

grown up out of a would-be Christmas tree plantation. Growing and selling valuable Christmas trees requires: prepping the field before planting; annual shearing and pruning to make them full and attractive; pest management, probably including herbicides, because monocultures are always prone to infestation; and serious marketing efforts to sell trees either wholesale or retail. Talk to experienced growers or attend a meeting of your state's Christmas tree association before taking the plunge.

MAPLE SYRUP

I've heard it said that people make syrup outside of New England and New York and adjacent Canada, but we can be forgiven for turning up our noses at it. Syrup from the Northeast is the best, and our sugarbushes are the most productive.

Retail prices for maple syrup vary widely from year to year and state to state, but the good news is that an eager market slurps up every drop of it. Sugar maples (though, increasingly red maples, too) are tapped in the spring, and their sap flows when a warm day follows a sub-freezing night. The sap is then boiled down to remove most of the water, and when it reaches 219°F and has a specific gravity of 67 Brix, it is ready to can as maple syrup.

Sugaring comes along at the end of a long cold winter and it involves roaring fires, sweet aromas, and tradition laced with camaraderie, so it's not a surprise that the romance of maple syrup draws in new sugarmakers like a vacuum pump draws sap on a 45-degree day in spring. You can go in head-over-heels or just maintain a mild flirtation. If you're in love, you'll tap your own trees, buy an evaporator and all the ancillary equipment, and build a sugarhouse for boiling. If you're feeling just a crush, you could tap your trees and sell the sap to a local sugarmaker. Or if it's just a mild flirtation, you could lease your woods to a sugarmaker, who would do all the tapping and sugarbush management in accordance with a clear agreement drawn up between you two. The revenues, of course, decline with the decreasing level of commitment and risk. ⊙

it contains many more pounds of wood. Furthermore, since the size of the firebox limits how much wood can be put into a wood stove, burning high-density species provides more heat from each refueling. That's why wood stove users prefer the oaks, hickories, sugar maple, beech, and yellow birch over medium-density woods such as red maple and white birch, and why low-density woods such as the aspens, basswoods, and most softwoods generally are not used for firewood unless other wood is not easily obtainable.

On a dollar-per-BTU basis, whether you harvest firewood on your own land or buy it cut, split, and delivered, firewood continues to be a bargain compared to other sources of heat.

PULPWOOD

Pulpwood is wood that will be turned into pulp, which is then made into paper or similar products. In addition to office paper and newsprint, pulp is used to make packaging materials, including corrugated cardboard, paperboard (the boxes your cereal or crackers come in), paper bags, and egg cartons.

A pulp mill uses a tremendous quantity of wood, typically hundreds of thousands to more than a million tons per year. While all tree species can be used to make pulp, different species (or groups of species) yield pulp with different qualities. Depending on the products they make, some pulp mills purchase a limited number of species while others accept a broader range.

Along with specifying the tree species they want, each mill specifies minimum and maximum diameters, lengths, and other criteria related to the processes the mill uses. These may include factors such as straightness and how well trimmed the logs need to be. In general, a load of pulpwood on a log truck has a more uniform look than a load of firewood. Logs that will be acceptable for a firewood processor might be too deformed to make it onto a pulp load.

In the past, pulpwood in the Northeast was usually bought in 4-foot lengths and measured by the cord. This made a lot of sense: most pulpwood was moved by hand and 4-foot-long pieces are a convenient length to handle, and the volume was easy to measure. Today, delivered wood is longer, and pulp is usually sold by the ton. (See the sidebar, *Wood Volume*, on page 76.)

The pulp and paper industry has traditionally been cyclical, though the current downturn may represent more permanent change. When the global economy is hot, demand exceeds supply, mills work around the clock, and prices for finished products increase. When the economy is slow, demand decreases, prices fall, and mills reduce output, and some might even close. The number of paper mills in the Northeast has decreased steadily in recent decades, though Maine and New York each continue to have several large mills that purchase significant volumes of pulpwood. Their demand for pulpwood, of course, follows the cyclical demand for paper products.

When the wood supply is tight, pulp mills expand their "wood basket" by paying higher prices and paying trucking allowances so they can get wood from greater distances. They may also relax the wood-quality standards a bit, accepting shorter or smaller-diameter logs and logs with more decay.

Pulpwood (or wood with the same characteristics) is also used by the manufacturers of engineered wood products, such as particle board, oriented strand panels, and flakeboard. The mills that make these products determine the suitable species and specifications for the material that works well for their process and products.

BIOMASS

Biomass is fiber that is used for the energy it provides. Switchgrass, corn, and other plant-based feedstocks grown for fuel are biomass, but let's focus our discussion on wood. We'll define biomass here as forest-grown wood (willow is one tree being grown in plantations) used for energy, either heat or electricity, and sometimes both.

There are some key differences between firewood and biomass. The first is the form of the fuel: wood stoves and small furnaces use large chunks of wood, whereas biomass is wood chipped or ground into small pieces. The chips flow and pour, which makes it easier to meter the fuel into the firebox, and they provide a large surface area for very rapid combustion.

Another difference is that the species of wood is relatively unimportant to the large-scale wood energy users. This opens the market to all tree species, both softwood and hardwood. And form doesn't matter in the least. Most systems are designed to use wood with relatively high moisture content, so drying is less important than for firewood.

A final difference is that the combustion is very carefully controlled in the large systems. Combustion is highly efficient, and scrubbers in smokestacks remove particulates from the flue gases. Air pollution from large wood-burning facilities is therefore very low.

When most people think of biomass, the image is that of the predominant method of processing, whole-tree chipping. Entire trees—right down to leaves and twigs—are transported in bunches by a grapple skidder to a landing. If sections of the trunk can be used for sawlogs, they are severed and put in a separate pile. After any higher-value products are separated, the rest of the tree is processed by feeding it into a chipper that shreds the tree and blows the chips into a tractor-trailer van.

A second production method more closely resembles the way pulpwood is processed into pulp-ready chips. Logs—not whole trees—are trucked to a chipping plant. The logs are debarked and the bark is sold for landscaping materials. The log is then chipped, which results in "clean chips," which are more valuable than whole-tree chips and can be used in smaller biomass boilers in schools and municipal buildings. If the species mix is controlled, these clean chips can also be sold to a pulp mill.

Biomass presents another market for low-quality trees, which can help make high-quality forest management more economically attractive. Demand is less seasonal than firewood, so it provides a relatively steady, year-round market. Purchasers buy large quantities (on the order of several hundred thousand tons per year for the typical electric power plant). A 30-megawatt plant will burn 390,000 tons of chips a year. In 2011, 20 wood-fired power plants were operating in the Northeast.

The bulk of the fiber the power plants use comes from whole-tree harvesting. Forest ecologists have voiced two major concerns over whole-tree harvesting: loss of coarse woody debris and loss of soil

wood volume

Depending on the market for the product, wood products are measured in one of three ways: board feet, cords, or green tons.

Board feet. Sawlogs and veneer logs are measured in board feet, which is determined by multiplying a board's length in feet by its nominal width in inches by its nominal thickness in inches and dividing the result by 12. A finished (rather than green) 2 x 4 measures 1.5 inches by 3.5 inches, but for calculating board feet, the nominal 2 x 4 dimensions are used. An 8-foot-long 2 x 4 contains 5.33 board feet: 2 x 4 x 8 divided by 12.

A board foot is a unit of measure for both lumber and logs. Since lumber is a rectangular cube and logs are cylindrical, that creates a challenge: there needs to be a way to translate the round into a measure of board feet. Formulas known as log rules have been created to determine the volume of lumber that can be expected to be produced from the log. Yes, this is odd, computing the volume of a solid cylinder by the expected yield of the cubic products within, but that's the system we use. And despite lumbermen and loggers and everyone else debating the merits of the more than a hundred log rules that have been devised, and whether log rules should even be used in the first place, this is what we have. In the Northeast, you'll find several different log rules used: the International ¼-inch rule, the Maine, the

Scribner, and the Doyle. In our discussion, we'll use International ¼-inch.

Because timber harvests produce thousands of board feet, an abbreviation has been developed for 1,000 board feet: MBF. An 8-foot log with a 12-inch diameter (measured at the small end inside the bark) contains 45 board feet. This would be expressed as .045 MBF. A truckload of hardwood logs like the one pictured at right with the one in Figure 4.9a holds approximately 6,600 board feet or 6.6 MBF. If it were carrying white pine, it could carry more and stay within the weight limits because 1.0 MBF of hardwood weighs 11,000 pounds, while 1.0 MBF of pine weighs no more than 9,000 pounds.

Cords. Contrast that orderly truckload with Figure 4.9b. This is the same size truck, and the firewood in it has an equivalent weight. Because firewood often comes from the tops of trees and from trees that aren't as straight as logs, it doesn't load as neatly as sawlogs or pulpwood. There's a lot of air in between the trees. This truck holds approximately 10 cords of wood. "Approximately" is an important word because the volume can't be fully determined until the wood is cut and stacked. A cord is a measure of wood 4 feet x 4 feet x 8 feet. It contains 128 cubic feet. The trucker will load his truck closer to the top of the rails and still be carrying the same payload. That's a lot of air in there.

Tons. The truck in Figure 4.9c is loaded with pulpwood. The logs are in 8-foot lengths, although most mills

Figure 4.9   a) A load of hardwood sawlogs totaling 6,600 board feet;
b) the same truck loaded with about 10 cords of firewood. Firewood logs are generally tree
length, and because of their rougher form, don't pack as tightly as the nearly cylindrical logs.
c) Pulp is loaded in designated lengths (these are 8 feet long), so despite the logs' poorer form,
a truckload of pulp looks more like a load of logs than a load of firewood;
d) a chip van filled with chipped biomass.

prefer longer lengths than the formerly customary 8-footers. Pulpwood used to be measured in cords, but it is more commonly measured in tons today. Wood contains more water—and thus weighs more—at certain times of the year, but let's assume that this tractor-trailer holds approximately 25 tons. In this case, I use approximately because I don't know the exact weight—that will be determined unequivocally when the truck crosses the scales, first loaded and then unloaded. The ambiguity inherent in log rules and firewood cords is gone with pulpwood where a ton is a ton is a ton. Except, of course, where it is a tonne.

A tonne is the metric ton, important to know because it's used in Canada, where some of your pulp might be sold depending on how far north you live. A tonne is 1,000 kilograms or 2,204.62 pounds.

Biomass chips are also measured by the ton. The chip van in Figure 4.9d holds somewhere between 25 and 35 tons depending on the species. It is weighed on scales just as the pulp trucks are. ⊙

This chart converts cords to green tons by species, and it works for pulpwood or for chips:

Estimated green tons per cord	
Pine	2.15
Hemlock	2.55
Hardwoods	2.70

nutrients. Trees that would otherwise be downed wood or snags providing cavities end up in the chip van because it's cost effective to remove everything. The Forest Guild, a national association of foresters dedicated to ecological forestry, advocates for retaining a certain percentage of snags, downed logs, and even some slash on whole-tree harvests. Nutrient loss can occur, they say, because the foliage and small branches contain most of the nutrients in the aboveground portion of trees. Is it wise to remove these nutrients from the forest ecosystem given the relatively small amount of additional biomass the leaves and twigs provide?

Some studies have backed up the claim of nutrient loss from whole-tree harvesting, while others have shown little negative impact to soil capacity. Further study of the potential for nutrient loss needs to be a priority.

The strongest argument in favor of whole-tree removal is in those situations where a forest's standing timber has such little commercial value that there's simply no other way to have any harvesting done. If there is little value recovered from a harvest, it becomes an expense to a landowner rather than a source of income. Whole-tree harvesting, with its capacity to remove large volumes of low-grade material, can break down that barrier to management activities. And once the "junk wood" is removed, the regeneration and the remaining trees have a chance to thrive.

Whole-tree harvesting should be used judiciously. Landowners and their foresters need to weigh the advantages of low harvesting costs against considerations of nutrient removal, the potential for increased damage to remaining trees, and other consequences for the forest ecosystem. It should be considered a tool to be used once on any particular piece of ground. Unless it can be documented that nutrient loss is not a significant problem, repeated harvests of whole trees cannot be justified.

THE FUTURE OF BIOMASS

Using wood for heat is much more efficient than using it to generate electricity. Wood-burning power plants capture 20 to 25 percent of the energy in the wood, whereas heating plants can be 70 percent efficient.

This points to the significant advantages that cogeneration offers. In these configurations, biomass is burned to simultaneously provide heat and generate electricity—you get the same operating efficiency of heat with the additional output of some electricity.

Cogeneration is not a new concept. For some time now, sawmills have been using their own waste wood—slabs, planer chips, sawdust—to heat the plant and provide some electricity. A number of colleges in the Northeast have developed cogeneration plants that extend the concept. The crucial factor is that the demand for heat must be local, so it has limited applicability. For one thing, most people in the rural Northeast live in individual houses spread too far apart across the landscape to be heated efficiently from a central facility. For another, siting new cogeneration plants in existing downtowns is sure to face tough zoning and public-relations battles.

In the processes discussed thus far, firewood and biomass are reduced to suitably sized pieces and burned without any further processing. There are some potential benefits to taking it one step further, and two processes have garnered much attention: wood pellets and cellulosic ethanol.

Wood pellets are made by grinding wood into sawdust, drying it to a low moisture content, and then extruding it to form small, uniformly sized pieces. The pellets are fuel for pellet stoves in homes and boilers for heating larger buildings. Burning pellets has advantages over firewood:

- Wood pellets are continuously conveyed into the stove or boiler, providing thermostatically controlled heat, which is analogous to oil or gas-fired stoves and boilers.
- Using wood pellets results in less mess.
- The automatic control of the combustion process results in less air pollution than occurs with typical wood stove operation.

There are disadvantages, too. Pellets require additional processing, which reduces the benefit of the lessened air pollution noted above. Setting up an efficient storage and delivery system (fuel hopper and auger) is expensive.

Changing cellulose—one of wood's major components—into ethanol (a type of alcohol) has gained lots of attention. Liquid fuels command a premium price, and there's great national interest in reducing fossil fuel use and decreasing our dependence on imported oil. Even though ethanol provides 10 percent less energy than gasoline, it will be an increasingly large part of the energy mix. Ethanol currently is produced from corn and other agricultural crops, and the processes for turning cellulose into ethanol show promise in trials. Will wood someday be a major part of the fuel in cars? That depends on how successful the technology is, how the price of other liquid fuels rises or falls over time, and how significantly federal and state governments encourage it through incentives and subsidies.

WHAT'S IT ALL WORTH?

It's always dangerous to publish prices, especially in a book designed to have a long shelf life. The price paid for wood is impossible to pinpoint because markets for wood fluctuate, and some regions lack competitive markets for certain products, which depresses prices—and sellers. Still, I'm willing to go out on a limb in an attempt to ground all of this in the reality of numbers. The prices discussed here held true in 2011 in central Vermont.

Trees range widely in value. A single high-end veneer log can be sold for the same price as a whole truckload of biomass. This is not an exaggeration. A 21-inch-diameter veneer log 8 feet long contains 155 board feet. At a price of $5,000/MBF (per thousand board feet) for the highest grade of slicer veneer, that log would bring in $775. A 25-ton trailer load of chips at $30 per ton would bring $750.

There is a wide range in prices paid for veneer logs. Logs destined for the inner cores of plywood and other low-value products might bring $150 per MBF, which is on the low end of sawlog prices. Appearance grade veneer, however, starts at $2,000/MBF and can reach $5,000/MBF. The rare log that meets veneer specifications for form and also has figure, such as bird's-eye maple, can fetch two or three times that. Don't fret about that happening to you—in my experience, these trees only grow on other people's woodlots.

The range in prices for chips is less dramatic, generally in the range of $20 to $40 per ton. The highest price is paid for clean chips that are sold for heat rather than electricity. Schools and some municipal complexes use these chips, which are more expensive because they have been processed to remove all the sawdust and oversize chunks.

In between veneer and chips are sawlogs, followed by firewood and pulpwood. Sawlog prices at the sawmill have a very large range, generally from around $150/MBF for low-end pallet logs to more than $1,000/MBF for large-diameter, high-quality hardwood logs of particularly desirable species. In recent years, prices have been more volatile than usual for some species. With all other conditions being equal, a log with a larger diameter is in a higher grade than one with a smaller diameter. A 16-inch-diameter 10-foot log with four clear faces might bring $1,200/MBF, while a log that looks exactly the same but is only 12 inches in diameter could bring $600. Not only does the 16-inch log have more volume—110 BF versus 55 BF—but it has a higher grade. One log brings $132, the other $33. In most cases, it pays to grow large trees. The exception is that white pine can be grown to

diameters too large for some sawmills to handle. To sell pine logs with diameters of 36 inches or more, you may have to find a specialty mill.

As for firewood, geographical anomalies account for whatever range there is in price per cord. Sold as a truckload of logs, firewood brings $70 to 100 per cord.

Pulpwood competes with both firewood and biomass. When the market is hot, it can even compete with low-end sawlogs. The final destination for a load of low-grade wood often depends simply on which buyer is closest. That's because the cost of trucking can eat away significantly at the delivered price. Even though it's in a different form, a truckload of pulpwood approximates a trailerload of chips both in weight and price per ton. Assume a load is 25 to 35 tons, and payment is $20 to $40 a ton.

All these prices are for delivered wood. They don't reflect any costs associated with logging, trucking, road-building, or forestry services. These will be covered in greater detail in Chapter 7, but in general, here's the bottom line.

Timber can be sold in a number of different ways, but no matter how it happens, the costs for harvesting and trucking are a direct cost, meaning that they are calculated per unit. They aren't higher or lower depending on the value of the product. What that means is that the portion left over for the landowner after expenses—known as stumpage—is much higher on the load of veneer than on the load of chips. In fact, the expenses on the chip harvest can be so high that the landowner is paid less than $1.00 per ton. So that 25-ton trailer load of chips might bring just $25 to the landowner. Send eight of those loads down the road, and you clear only $200. In some circumstances, the landowner might receive nothing for the chipwood.

This discrepancy creates the temptation to harvest only the valuable products, and it's this temptation that has resulted in many impoverished woodlots. High-grading has been part of the harvesting culture for generations. It takes concerted effort to convince people to do the opposite, to harvest the junk wood for little money today in the interest of a more valuable woodlot tomorrow. Good land managers have proven that it does make sense, and the rewards will come to those who are able to think in forest time.

The most fantastic aspect of a forest is that it has great value as a whole, and that value is not diminished when component products like trees and sap are taken from it, provided it's done with care and forethought. When it is, the financial part of the value equation can work out very nicely. ◘

CHAPTER 5

A PLAN FOR THE FUTURE

At this stage of the game, you are equipped with two very important bodies of knowledge. First, you know your woods: you have an understanding of the condition of your forest, its history, and what it holds in terms of inventory from both a timber and an ecological perspective. Second, you understand the full gamut of products available from the forest, both the tangible and the more abstract. Now it's time to bring the two together and ponder what might be possible on your land.

Having a positive influence on the condition and future direction of your forest is one of the most satisfying and rewarding experiences we landowners can have. Tending a piece of land, using products from that land in your own life or selling them to local businesses, noticing that new songbirds are singing from your treetops, seeing your family and visitors getting pleasure from being out in your woods—these are the rewards of doing good work in your forest.

But those rewards don't happen by accident. Every woodland owner benefits from going through the process necessary to produce a written management plan, even if the act of writing is done by your consulting forester. Discussing it and thinking it all through will help you clarify what you would like to have happen on your land.

A management plan deals with past, present, and future. In Chapter 3, we covered the descriptive summary. This contains the forester's assessment of the land use history, gleaned largely from observations of your land and experience with similar parcels in the vicinity. It also paints a picture of the present, backed up by data taken from the timber cruise and the nature cruise. The cruises are the scouting missions; from them a plan of action can be developed. The plan then describes the future actions that will be taken on the land to steer it toward accomplishment of certain goals and objectives.

The woodland exam we discussed in Chapter 3 is a useful first step. Woodland exams tend to be more qualitative than quantitative, and they give the owner a feeling for possible next steps in the management process at a very reasonable cost. A woodland exam is good to have, but it's not a real management plan.

Your woodland is a valuable asset, and actions taken in it should be considered in an organized, systematic, and informed way. In the absence of clearly defined objectives for the land, many woodland owners have succumbed to the temptation to act spontaneously when presented with what seems like a golden opportunity. A knock at the door presents an offer of $10,000 (or some other attractive number) for thinning the woods out back, which seems like a fortune for something you don't deem that valuable. Save your spontaneity for social occasions. Otherwise, you could be compromising your woodlot's future value, and the attractive offer could be for a fraction of what the wood is really worth. With a management plan in place, opportunity knocks according to a set schedule and with specific strategies and objectives in mind.

Some owners have given considerable thought to the future of their forest and have a mental catalogue of what they intend or hope to do on the land. That's laudable, but it's no substitute for a written plan. Without committing a plan to paper, it's just too easy to wing it and end up straying from the course. Part of the resistance to a written plan is often an unwillingness to pay a forester to prepare one. Here are some more reasons to go to the expense of a management plan:

- If you want to enroll in your state's current use tax program and reduce your property tax bill, most states require a written management plan. So do most other government programs and opportunities.
- The process will help to clarify what is most important to you and put the possibilities into a realistic framework.

- Having a plan and the inventory it includes will make it much easier to reduce the tax you pay when you receive income from cutting timber.
- Land that's being managed according to a plan is more valuable to all those who currently own it or who may own it in the future: you, if you keep your land; your heirs, if you pass it on; a buyer, if you plan to sell it; and a land trust, if you are considering a long-term conservation strategy.
- Yes, you can deviate from your plan, but having it in place will make you evaluate and justify any changes.

There is no single standard management plan format. Each state has particular requirements for participants in its current use or forest stewardship program, and these can vary dramatically. All plans, however, need to be written in the language of silviculture. That's why a forester's advice is crucial. If you don't know the difference between even-aged and uneven-aged management or between thinning and single tree selection, you won't be able to write a plan that a state forestry official can approve.

A plan written as a requirement of participation in a current use program is enforceable. If you are in violation of the spirit of the plan (and sometimes the letter), you may be forced to withdraw and suffer any consequences, and the consequences are real.

There are all kinds of plans, varying with the size and heterogeneity of the property, as well as with the complexity and specificity of ownership objectives. Some plans are brief and primarily descriptive; others are highly detailed, with a lot of quantitative information and detailed appendices. Plans required for participation in third-party certification programs, such as Tree Farm or the Forest Stewardship Council (FSC), must address a list of specific topics. Regardless of its length or complexity, a plan customarily includes maps, stand data, a description of the forest, and a plan for the future. This takes into consideration ownership objectives, and it outlines a series of scheduled activities to achieve the objectives.

Oh, yes, objectives. A forester who is working with you to create a management plan for your land is likely to pepper you with questions about your goals and objectives. But many forestland owners haven't really given it that much thought. When faced with open-ended questions such as "What are your goals for your woodland?" many don't have a ready response. If you are like most people, you own forestland primarily because you enjoy living in the country. You relish the privacy, peace and quiet, and a nice place to walk. Does that rise to the level of goals and objectives?

Whether you've thought about it much or not, all of us have some goals for our land. The challenge is to articulate them. Your forester should ask questions that will help ascertain your wishes, while keeping in mind the capacity of the land to fulfill them. The plan will need to balance the two.

What kinds of questions can you expect your forester to ask? Here are some likely ones:

- Many people say they would like to leave their place better than when they found it. If this motivates you, in what way would you measure that? In what aspects of the complex forest would you want to see your improvements made manifest? Timber, songbirds, game animals, trails, firewood?

- Would you like to grow better timber that has more commercial value, making the forest itself more valuable?

- How often do you spend time in your woods? When you're there, what do you do?

- Do you have substantial diversity of wildlife habitat in place? If not, would you want to make your land more diverse?

- Do you have specific sites where the soils are good and the trees are well formed and growing particularly well? If so, would you be interested in managing those sites specifically to take advantage of their potential?

- How long will owning this land be important to you? Do you have an heir apparent who would like to own it? If not, what will you do with it?

- Speaking of money, how do your finances fit into this? How important is it that the woodlot provide occasional income to help defray the costs of owning it? Do you have enough security that you can forgo any real income for the moment with the idea that you are trying to make this asset appreciate in value? Could you in fact put some resources into it, by paying for some timber stand improvement or better access?

- Are there particular species of animals that mean something to you? Would you like to improve the prospects for them? Ask your forester if your land has the right conditions for them.

- What about sugarmaking? Do you have an interest in tapping some maples?

- Are there parts of your land that are relatively inaccessible? Is that a plus or a minus? Would you like to improve access or leave those areas remote and free from human activity?
- Would your family be more likely to enjoy the land if it had a network of trails?
- Are there any natural areas—vernal pools or other wetlands—you'd like to protect? Did anything come up in your nature cruise checklist that you want to pay special attention to? Any legacy trees?
- What about cultural artifacts? Do you have any stone walls, cellar holes, dug wells, or stone fence posts that mean something to you?
- What about firewood? Do you want your woods to provide a readily accessible annual allotment of firewood? Would you be interested in cutting some each year for your own use?
- What is your favorite place on the property? Do you want to make that spot even more significant? Would you be more interested in leaving it alone or making improvements to it?
- Would you like to have more species of songbirds using the woods?
- Has your forester told you that there are sections of your woodlot that have so little potential value that it's better to start over? Are you willing to clearcut a section to accomplish this? What if you could do it in stages?
- Would a tent platform or lean-to make you more likely to camp out on the land? Where would you place it?
- Do you hunt? Would you like to make the land more hospitable to turkeys? To deer? To grouse and woodcock? To snowshoe hare?

Figure 5.1 a) Foresters use both old tools (the Biltmore stick measures diameter) and new. *b)* This forester is entering inventory data into a hand-held computer. *Photo a) by Eben McLane. Photo b) courtesy of Forecon.*

- What about trails? How would you be most likely to use them: ride an ATV, cross-country ski, mountain bike, ride your horse, walk the dog, train for a marathon?
- Will you sell your forestland someday? If so, would you like to build its timber value until then? Or would you prefer to tap into the timber value before a sale? There are ways to do this without irreparably affecting long-term value.

At this time, you don't have to know how to implement your objectives. That's what your forester is for. You'll learn more as you go, but your job today is simply to express clearly what's important to you.

If you would like some immediate income to help cover the cost of the management plan, discuss this with your forester. In many cases, it's possible to harvest some timber now without compromising the future value of your woodland. Covering up-front costs makes a lot of sense. Resist, however, the temptation to think only in the short term. Trees take many decades to grow to maturity, so your management plan needs to be for the long term.

MANAGEMENT PLAN ELEMENTS

- Descriptive summary including information on stand history and soils
- Map delineating stands
- Map placing the land in its larger context
- Timber inventory
- Plan of activities
- Schedule of treatments

GOALS AND OBJECTIVES

Your plan should include both goals and objectives. Goals are broad and provide direction to the overall stewardship effort, expressing the hopes and vision of the owner. Goals might sound something like these:

1. Build standing timber value in order to pass on an appreciated forest asset to heirs, while developing a network of trails for recreation.
2. Provide as wide a range of wildlife habitat features as possible, while producing enough firewood to heat

the house and occasional timber revenue to cover property taxes.

An objective is more detailed and provides the foundation for activities on specific areas within the boundaries of the property. An area or stand-level objective is much more specific. For example:

1. Produce high-quality spruce sawlogs while maintaining an adequate visual buffer to maintain privacy.
2. Increase the complexity of the forest structure without compromising long-term timber value.

Notice that in both goals and objectives, the sentence structure includes a primary intention and what might be considered a byproduct. Let's look at these in order:

Goals 1 and 2 are simple. Trails are a byproduct of the intermediate treatments that are leading to increased value of standing timber. Firewood and timber revenue are secondary to the main goal of wide range of habitat.

Objective 1 starts to introduce some nuance. Producing spruce sawlogs is a goal, but in certain circumstances that could run counter to the secondary goal of the visual buffer. If by taking spruce, you are promoting regeneration of hardwoods rather than softwoods, your buffer will be compromised. On the other hand, your objectives could dovetail perfectly if you make sure that the regeneration is primarily spruce, so that sapling- and pole-sized evergreens, with their thick foliage, act as an effective hedge.

Objective 2 also has some nuance. A more complex structure is important, as evidenced by its being stated first. But

green certification

In the early 1990s, an international movement developed based on the premise that much of the world's forestland was being logged illegally or irresponsibly.

These activists developed the idea that by creating standards for management and granting a seal of approval to the lands that were well managed, the overall quality of management would improve because the seal of approval would be seen as significant. Thus was born the Forest Stewardship Council (FSC), an international non-profit organization that has developed the FSC label to signify sustainable management.

The FSC established protocols for tracking the chain of custody of the wood from the forest to the finished product so that products with the FSC label could be shown to have been made according to high standards. It was hoped that certified landowners and companies along the green chain of custody would be rewarded in the marketplace by consumers who would be willing to pay more for products with the FSC label.

Sustained yield was the mantra of the early forestry movement in this country: Manage forests in a way that removed only a sustainable amount over time, so that long into the future the forests will be capable of yielding the same volume of timber. That timber-centric focus has given way to a broader concept of the sustainability of the system, and FSC has played a role in promoting this thinking.

It didn't take long for the forest products industry to see FSC as a threat, so the large producers in the United States—mainly paper companies—developed their own certification system. This system, called the Sustainable Forestry Initiative (SFI), differed initially from FSC in that it required only a voluntary adherence to a set of standards. This amounted to little more than self-certifying, which contrasted greatly with FSC's rigorous standards and independent third-party certification.

Recognizing that they had mis-played their hand, the member companies of SFI created an independent board that developed its own system of third-party auditing. Today, professionals who audit for both FSC and SFI see very little difference between the two sets of standards. They are both credible systems with high standards of performance. SFI followed suit also in developing its own chain of custody program. In the Northeast, several large landowners today are certified under both systems.

Where did all this leave the family forest owner? Out in the cold essentially. It was too expensive to go through the process of certifying a relatively small acreage, so few family forest owners bothered with it. One solution to the problem is group certification, a concept pioneered by Vermont

Family Forests (VFF). VFF pooled the holdings of a number of different landowners, all of whom agreed to abide by FSC standards and have their compliance verified independently. Building on this concept, FSC began to make it possible for consulting foresters—resource managers—to form groups of forest owners that could gain group certification. As of 2011, only a small number of these groups have been formed.

One group of certified landowners predated this movement, the American Tree Farm System. It had been in operation since 1941, but it was more of an educational and support organization through which Tree Farmers learned from other landowners and from experts how best to manage their woods for timber, wildlife, recreation, and water quality. As a certification system, it suffered from a lack of credibility (similar to SFI in its early days) because the foresters inspecting and certifying the management were usually the same foresters who were managing the land.

Tree Farm took its own steps to change this lack of accountability, and inspections became more rigorous and conformed to another set of international standards, the Programme for the Endorsement of Forest Certification (PEFC). Along with SFI, Tree Farm has, since 2008, had its certification program under the umbrella of PEFC, which is the world's largest certifier of forestlands.

The jury is still out on forest certification. It has not put more dollars in the pockets of certified landowners. Instead, rather than receiving a premium for their forest products, certified landowners have gained access to some important markets. They won't get shut out of markets that demand certified sources, which is a concern to large landowners, whose ability to sell wood year-round is crucial.

A consortium of paper buyers led by Time, Inc., requires that paper the members buy comes only from certified sources. This requirement has led to the certification of many millions of acres owned by large landowners, which is clearly a positive development because it means these lands are being managed according to high standards.

Owners of certified forests can sell their wood to those buyers who demand certified wood. It's just that there aren't that many of these buyers because the market is still in its infancy in the United States. Finally, there are plenty of well-managed forests whose owners have resisted the pressure to have their lands certified, and who have not suffered financially for their choice. Forest certification will live or die based on perceived economic benefit. ⊙

let's not accomplish that by prematurely cutting trees that have potential value. Instead, increase the structural diversity by removing clumps of poorly formed trees.

Not all goals and objectives can be stated or need to be stated with this sentence construction in mind, but it can be helpful to think about management in these terms. If you focus on a particular goal or objective, there will be other consequences. Some are positive effects that you want to enhance; others are negative that you'll want to avoid or minimize.

In essence, we manage our woods in order that they can be more productive. And it's crucial to note that by productive, I am referring to the full spectrum of products we discussed in the last chapter—not only sawlogs but also habitat for snowshoe hare or black-throated blue warblers.

Each choice that you make will favor some species of trees at the expense of others and some species of animals at the expense of others. Working with what you have—which you have by now determined through your various cruises—you can enhance or modify current conditions.

Forest time is not human time, so some of the changes you are making will require generations to be fully realized. On the other hand, some vegetative responses happen almost immediately. Plants and trees respond quickly to increased light. The stark scene of a forest the day the skidders are loaded on a trailer and driven away is ephemeral. Within a year, the vegetation will come back and cloak the browns and grays with a covering of green.

One last thought about working with a forester. Your forester is a technical specialist who will ask you lots of good questions, help you put together a good plan that meets your objectives, let you know about conflicts among objectives, answer your questions, and tell you when you're being unrealistic. Your forester should not finalize a plan or schedule any activities without your participation and approval. After all, you and your forester are partners in this undertaking. Don't be surprised to see your forester become just as enthusiastic, just as committed to your woodlands as you are. Most foresters have a great capacity to become devoted to the forests they manage. It can be an occupational hazard for some when a woodlot they've managed for years is sold and subsequently exploited. It's like losing a friend.

FROM PLAN TO ACTION

A plan is both a roadmap and an hourglass. It's easy for a well-intentioned forest owner to have a gung-ho attitude about what can be accomplished and how soon. Take the plan seriously, but schedule activities realistically. It's better to be conservative in scheduling work.

That work can be classified several ways, none more basic than "commercial" versus "noncommercial." In the Northeast, commercial activities almost always involve harvesting something: trees, for certain, but also sap, blueberries, balsam, laurel, or witch hazel. These often involve hiring a contractor to do the work, though who would ask someone else to harvest their blueberries?

Noncommercial activities are those that are designed to make the forest more valuable but don't produce immediate income. They include planting trees, killing trees in place to favor others, pruning, building roads, conducting a prescribed burn, controlling invasive plants, preparing a site for seeding, and maintaining or creating a particular habitat. Many landowners balk at incurring expenses (ah, that's what we mean by noncommercial) to achieve a forest management objective. But if the noncommercial work is accomplished in conjunction with a timber sale, the cost can be offset. Access improvements, such as road construction or upgrades, can sometimes be incorporated into a commercial activity such as a timber sale. When the logger's equipment is on your land, it's always good to try to figure out what else might be accomplished.

Another way to make noncommercial improvements is through cost-share contracts, which are sometimes available through state or federal programs that reimburse you for some of the cost of noncommercial activities. Some activities (crop tree pruning, precommercial thinning, and the labor of tree planting) can be accomplished without spending money if you're willing to invest your time and sweat.

Forest management plans typically cover a multi-year period, often ten to fifteen years. The intervals for plan updating, redoing the inventory, and boundary updating should be specified in the plan. Depending on your objectives and conditions in the forest, a logical sequence of activities may be obvious, or you may have to struggle with how you will prioritize the work. For activities that will require investment of money or your time, do not commit to them in the plan unless you are really willing to commit to them in the woods. Separate planned activities into two baskets: required and optional. Within each basket, separate into higher and lower priority groups. Estimate any costs. If you will need to locate and engage any contractors, be sure to start the process early enough. Revenue-producing activities such as timber sales should be flexibly scheduled to avoid down markets and take advantage of favorable markets. ◘

CHAPTER 6

FORESTRY 101: INTRO TO SILVICULTURE

Trees are the defining characteristic of a forest. No trees, no forest. It's not only the simple presence of trees, but their size and their concentration that make them so important. Trees dominate forests and exert more influence on the forest's ecology than any other organisms. Consequently, most forest management has traditionally been concerned with making adjustments to the quantity, condition, age, and quality of a forest's trees. That emphasis is changing, and more foresters are comfortable acknowledging that forestry does not begin and end with the cultivation of trees. Still, growing and tending trees is at the heart of a forester's work.

This chapter is the most technical one in the book. As its title suggests, it serves as an introduction to silviculture, but it's not written for forestry students, it's written for landowners. The further your interest in managing your forest takes you, the more beneficial a grounding in silviculture becomes, because it's important that you and your forester can speak the same language. I hope you will enjoy delving into the nitty-gritty of silviculture, but if you find yourself mystified, feel free to move on to the next chapter and return later when you are looking for reference materials.

IDEAL CONDITIONS FOR GROWTH

Sunlight is the energy source for trees. The goal of silviculture is to grow healthy, vigorous trees that exhibit good form—a straight trunk and a crown full enough to absorb light for photosynthesis.

If we were to arrange optimal conditions for growing the perfect tree, we would provide a site that's a perfect match for the tree's silvical needs. It would begin its life in strong competition from similar-sized trees. I'm partial to sugar maple, so let's assume the tree is a sugar maple seedling growing in a pure stand of at least 7,000 other maples on 1 acre. Like its cohorts, this seedling is less than 1 inch in diameter and stands a little more than 1 foot tall. It grows in these close quarters for 10 or so years and develops into a sapling. The continued competition forces the tree to grow straight, and as it puts on height, it self-prunes, which means it sheds its lower branches because their leaves no longer receive sufficient light.

a)

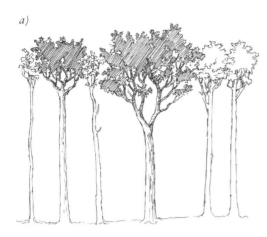

b)

Figure 6.1 a) The two shaded crowns are both dominant trees, but the one on the right has a strong healthy crown. The one on the left would benefit from thinning out the two adjacent trees. *b)* The crown on the center white pine is optimal in both breadth and height. It is suppressing the adjacent trees.

It will take another 10 to 15 years for the sapling to reach pole size—a diameter of 5 inches—and, adhering to Darwinian principles, the most vigorous trees will suppress the less vigorous, relegating them to the understory and then death. The process of self-pruning continues, and the sugar maple develops clear, knot-free wood in its trunk. If the lower branches were to continue living, they would show up as knots throughout the trunk, reducing the tree's utility and its value (when the tree is cut later). We're trying to produce a long, straight trunk free of limbs for 40 feet, instead of one resembling a yard tree, whose stout lower branches would entice generations of climbing children.

Standing slightly above its nearest competition, the perfect sugar maple's expanding crown helps it continue to put on girth. Then, as if they were involved in a single elimination tournament, the winners of each round move on to compete with each other. Instead of competing with trees 2 or 3 feet away, the trees now compete with those 8 or 10 feet away. The same principle applies that got the tree off to a good start—competition (but not too much) fosters strong, straight, valuable growth. With the trees now 35 to 45 years old, the contest is carried out among fewer but larger trees.

At this time, when less than one-third of the tree's height is made up of a live crown, we intervene for the first time. We'll choose the keepers and remove those that are inferior in form. The goal of the initial thinning is to maintain the favored tree's good growth rate by giving the crown room to expand but not so much room that it

the importance of site

Trees grow in three significant ways: diameter, crown, and height.

The goal of management is to increase the tree's diameter by making sure its crown can use the sun's energy effectively. Management influences the size of the crown and the trunk.

Height, on the other hand, is predetermined by the site on which the tree grows. The site conditions—soil fertility, aspect (which direction the slope faces), and moisture availability—will determine how well a particular species will grow there because each species has definite silvical preferences.

Foresters compare growing conditions by using site index, an assigned value that predicts the height that a free-to-grow tree of a particular species will reach at age 50 on that site. A good growing site for sugar maple has a site index of 70 or higher, which means a 50-year-old tree will be 70 feet tall on that site. Assuming the site index is correct, there's nothing you can do to make a tree grow taller than its site index suggests. Unless you were to bring in fertilizer—which is rarely, if ever, done in the Northeast—management does not influence height.

You can also evaluate a site by observing the species of trees that are growing well on it. For instance, within the northern hardwood family of trees—dominated by sugar maple, American beech, and yellow birch—the presence or absence of certain species can tell you if a site is good or poor. If along with sugar maple, you find white ash or basswood, it's a good site, probably a 70 for sugar maple. If it lacks ash and basswood but holds yellow birch and beech, it's only a moderately rich site, corresponding to a 60 to 70 site index for sugar maple. And if there are plenty of red maple and spruce-fir joining the beech, it's poorer still. On sites like the latter, you will not be able to grow demanding species like sugar maple and cherry, but you can still grow fine specimens of the trees that are adapted to these sites.

Red oak is a valuable tree whose needs are less demanding, and it can grow well on sites where sugar maple or cherry would lag behind. A good red oak site might include these hardwoods as a minor component. ☉

compromises the continued development of a clear bole. If crown space is opened up too soon, the tree might develop new branches (called epicormic branches) on the trunk that has already pruned itself. It is important to give each crop tree space to grow at the appropriate time. The tree will respond by expanding its crown (and thus its capacity for photosynthesis) and increasing the trunk's diameter at a faster rate. Guidelines have been established for creating the optimal density for growing trees. These guidelines are known as stocking guides, and I'll get to them shortly.

Fifteen or so years later, when the crop trees have tall, clear boles and the diameter growth has slowed, we intervene again by identifying the best trees and removing any competing trees that have poorly formed boles or crown structures that are compromised and at risk of splitting. Now instead of pole-sized trees, we have trees that have reached the sawtimber stage with 12-inch diameters. They are becoming more valuable each year. Given room, their growth rate increases again, and they will need another thinning in the future.

Finally, when the crop tree reaches its maturity—100 years or more for a sugar maple—it has developed into a veneer-quality tree worth hundreds of dollars. In a perfect situation, that process is happening throughout the acre, and from a starting point of more than 7,000 stems, an acre can produce 75 perfect 20-inch diameter trees. That's a lot of value.

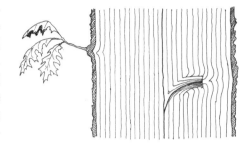

Figure 6.2   This cross section of a tree shows an epicormic branch on the left. It starts from a bud on the bark when the tree has a flood of light reaching it after it has grown to considerable size. Contrast that with the early branch in the center that has been grown over with several years of clear wood.

DOMINANCE

Let's dig more deeply into some silvicultural concepts and terminology as we go forward. In any forest, trees that have grown together establish a hierarchy or pecking order.

- Some trees will be *dominant*, blessed by genetics or the luck of the draw to pull ahead of neighbors and establish a strong, dominant crown. Since photosynthesis is the engine of tree growth, larger crowns are the mark of the favored, and a dominant tree is one whose crown captures sunlight from above and from the sides. It basks in the glory of its prominence.

- *Co-dominant* might seem like a misnomer because these trees are not co-equal with the dominant, but the term works

if you look at it as you would a pilot and a co-pilot. The latter stands ready to take over. A co-dominant's crown receives direct sunlight from above, but because its sides are crowded by others, it doesn't get as much sunlight from the sides as the dominants do. This position in the canopy shows great promise.

- Moving down in the scale of crown class, we reach the *intermediate* group, which is defined as those trees whose crowns have reached into the canopy but that get little if any direct light either from above or the sides. It's a challenge for these trees to grow vigorously, and depending on the species, too much languishing in the shadows might stress them out and make them vulnerable.

- Last are the *suppressed* trees, whose existence is as sorry as it sounds. They have been overtopped, and as a result, their growth rate and vigor are suppressed. These trees have little chance to shine, and if they were suddenly to find themselves the only ones left standing, the shock might kill them. That's not a joke, by the way.

Trees with dominant crowns have a leg up and will outcompete the others. That's great if the crown is sound and the bole is well-formed, but that's not always the case. Sometimes crowns can be compromised by the way they've branched. If the crown is at risk of splitting because of a V-shaped fork, or if the tree's bole is poorly formed, then the tree will be removed in a thinning. The same evaluation is given to co-dominant trees. With good crowns and the potential for sawlogs, they can gain tremendously from thinning, and the best candidates stay in the mix. Intermediate trees might have some hope, more so if they are hemlocks, spruce, or sugar maple, the few species that can respond well to more sunlight after a period of languishing. Suppressed trees will never be more than pulp or BTUs. These low-grade trees can be removed in a timber sale, if there are markets for them.

Figure 6.3   Crown classes. The single *dominant* (D) crown rules this patch of woods, followed by the two *co-dominant* (C) trees to the right. The five *intermediate* (I) trees still have a chance to grow well, but the *suppressed* (S) trees will never amount to much.

STOCKING

In forestry, stocking refers to how completely trees are occupying a forest site. The more trees of a given size there are on an acre, the less each tree will be able to grow in diameter each year because each will receive a smaller percentage of the energy. An important tool of forest management, therefore, is manipulating stand density so that tree growth is concentrated in the most desirable trees.

Basal area is a measure of the amount of space taken up by the trunks of trees on a per acre basis. Rather than a percentage, it is calculated in square feet, and the measurement is the cross section of

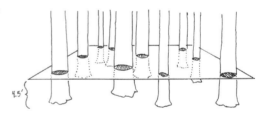

Figure 6.4   The cumulative area of the cross sections of trees in this horizontal plane 4.5 feet above the ground represents the *basal area*.

trees in a plane 4 ½ feet above the ground. (This height is known as breast height, and it's the height at which tree diameters are measured. To all who speak forestry, that measurement is known as diameter at breast height, or DBH.) Picture an acre of trees with an invisible plane intersecting them at breast height. The area of all of these circular cross sections combine to form a composite square footage, and

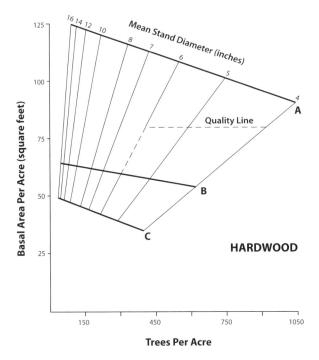

Figure 6.5   The stocking chart for even-aged northern hardwood stands. The A-line is fully stocked, the B-line is suggested residual stocking. The C-line is minimum stocking. The quality line is the density required to produce high quality stems of beech, sugar maple, yellow birch, and red maple. Source: *Silvicultural Guide for Northern Hardwood Types in the Northeast* (revised), Northeastern Forest Experiment Station, Research Paper NE-603.

it's expressed as square feet per acre. For any given basal area, if the tree diameters are larger, there are fewer trees per acre. The same basal area could result from a few large trees or many small trees.

The stocking charts—we're showing the one for northern hardwoods, but they exist for mixedwood forests, white pine, and hemlock as well—show the relationship between mean stand diameters, number of trees per acre, and the basal area. The stocking of any stand can be represented by a point on the graph at the confluence of two measurements: the basal area per acre and the number of trees per acre. These data are accumulated when a forester conducts the timber cruise. You'll notice three lines labeled A, B, and C. The A line represents a fully stocked stand; above this level, trees will start to die. The B line is the stocking level at which the greatest number of trees will put on the best growth in board feet. At the C line, the site is being underutilized.

Let's put that into perspective. Picture a football field, which conveniently measures close to 1 acre. A stand with a basal area of 125 square feet per acre

V doesn't mean victory

If you look up at the crowns of your trees, you will see at least one place where a tree forks into two.

It can fork in two different ways: the fork is shaped either like a V or a U.

The V is a risky shape because it's inherently unstable. It may be fine when the tree is small, but as each of the stems expands, part of its expansion is toward the other. This situation is known as included bark, and the bark on each stem stands as a barrier to joining together.

As each stem puts on diameter, it may have no place to put the wood except in a bulging formation that looks like wings. Trees with wings are highly susceptible to flying away. When a brisk wind comes from exactly the wrong direction, one of the fork's stems will snap off. The result is a crown that is reduced by half and a gaping wound of exposed wood. Trees with V forks are prime candidates for removal in a thinning.

If the fork forms a U, it is much more stable. Both sides of the U are growing on their own, each of them branching out and contributing to a full crown. ⊙

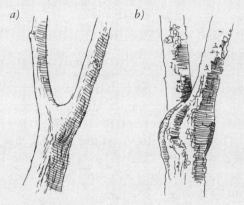

Figure 6.6   a) The U-shaped fork is stable. Both sides of the fork can add mass without risk. *b)* The V-shaped fork, on the other hand, is at risk of splitting at the seam.

is densely stocked; at 30 square feet per acre, it would be very lightly stocked. A single sheet of plywood measures 32 square feet; four of them are 128 square feet. Place one sheet of plywood on one football field and put four sheets on another football field. Given that an acre is 43,560 square feet, that difference in coverage might not seem significant, but in forestry terms it is a huge difference—if those sheets were instead the combined cross sections of trees, they would represent the range between understocked and overstocked.

Let's go back to the acre I described above in which we were growing the perfect crop tree. We'll use that hypothetical acre to show how the stocking guides work. In this stand, we conduct our initial thinning when the stand is 35 to 45 years old and the trees are at the larger end of the pole class. Looking up, you would see that the crowns completely fill the canopy. In a previously unmanaged hardwood forest like this, we can expect it to be fully stocked, at the A line or even slightly above. If you take a look at the illustration, you'll see how that plays out.

In practice, a forester would measure basal area using a prism at predetermined points in the timber cruise and would tally the "count trees" and take their diameter measurements. In this case, he calculates that there are 330 trees per acre and that the average basal area is 122. The point on the chart where those two numbers meet is just above the A line, confirming that this forest is fully stocked, and slightly to the left of the 8-inch diameter diagonal line. So the mean stand diameter is between 8 and 9 inches DBH. Judging from the branching pattern in their crowns, the trees have reached their maximum merchantable height, so at this point, they can be given more space.

As a general rule, a thinning will reduce the stocking by about one-third, but not with an initial thinning. This first cut in a previously unmanaged stand has to be undertaken with caution so the residual stocking will remain midway between the A line and the B line. The goal of this first thinning would be to remove undesirable trees, particularly low-value species and poorly formed or damaged and otherwise compromised trees. How many would you cut? In a first cut, many foresters would decide to reduce the stocking by 35 square feet per acre, with a target basal area of 90 for the residual stand. To accomplish that, they would mark enough trees to be cut to bring the stocking to 90 square feet of basal area. They wouldn't do it by counting trees but by using a 10-factor prism to determine what 90 square feet would be.

Essentially, what the forester does to thin the stand down to 90 square feet is to remove the equivalent of three registering trees at any point. See the illustration on page 46 in Chapter 3 for an explanation of how the prism is used. In practice, it's more complicated than that, but that is a perfectly reasonable image to keep in mind.

Fifteen years pass, the trees' trunks have increased in diameter and their crowns have expanded to where they once again have to compete for the light, so it's time to conduct a second thinning. At this point, the trees will have put on as many as 3 or 4 inches in diameter because they've been given access to more of the site's resources. Tree growth brings the basal area back toward the A line, and the stocking is now 110 square feet. We'll feel free to be a bit more aggressive at this point. With a mean diameter of 12 inches, the target basal area is about 70. So this thinning will bring it back from 110 feet to 70 feet.

Each time you do a thinning, you do so with a set of marking guidelines in mind. Here's an example of guidelines for the thinning we've just spoken of that will reduce it to 70 square feet. We would remove:

- Trees at risk. Valuable trees that will not last until the next thinning, or that can be expected to degrade significantly

- Unacceptable stems. Trees that will not produce a sawlog now or in the future due to defective form

- Undesirable species

- Acceptable stems crowding high-value stems

Figure 6.7   a) The tree on the right is 10 inches DBH. The two trees closest to it are both 6 inches DBH. Despite their difference in size, these trees are all the same age. In *b)*, the four cross sections were cut from trees of the same age, all within a year or two of 73 years. All got started after the Hurricane of 1938 blew down the larger trees above them. The smallest tree was 4.5 inches in diameter, the largest 9.25 inches.

In doing so, you will be removing trees in the main canopy, including some dominant and co-dominant trees. And as a result, you will be providing adequate space for the stems that have the highest potential to produce high-value sawlogs and veneer. You are also removing suppressed and intermediate trees of poor form.

Note that you might not be removing all of the trees that fit the guidelines. You are removing the volume that will bring the basal area to 70 square feet. If that means you have to leave some acceptable stems crowding high-value stems, you do it because they are there to provide forest structure.

Manipulating the density in which trees grow is a primary tool in forestry. It accelerates what would happen naturally, and it means the forester chooses the winners and losers.

TWO KINDS OF FORESTS

In traditional forestry, there are two kinds of forests. Any forest you step into fits one of these two categories: even-aged or uneven-aged. These either-or designations seem fairly straightforward.

In an even-aged forest, most of the trees are within a decade or two of being the same age. There are a few ways this condition can come about:

- It can result from a stand-leveling natural disturbance. In the inland Northeast, hurricanes are rare, but many current stands in New England originated in the wake of the 1938 hurricane.

- An even-aged forest could also come about when land that was formerly agricultural, either cropland or pastureland, stopped being used for that purpose. When the tractor or the cows retire, trees take over the previously open land, with most of them seeding in within a period of less than 20 years, which is the approximate time span for the even-aged designation to hold true.

- The third way an even-aged stand could come about is through a clearcut. All the trees were removed over an extensive area, and the trees that regenerated—either from seeds, stump sprouts, or seedlings and saplings already present—did so within a short window of time.

Technically, an even-aged forest can include one other age cohort within it, but for most of the stand's life, it's limited to one. The second cohort would consist of regenerating trees that are established either through specific silvicultural choices or naturally when the canopy begins to collapse, as often happens when it's made up of pioneer species like aspen or paper birch.

In contrast, an uneven-aged forest contains trees of at least three distinct age classes. It's important to remember that age and size are not the same. Suppressed trees can have skinny diameters compared to their dominant neighbors of the same age. You can often tell their relative age from their bark, since older suppressed trees have gnarled, thicker bark because the trees haven't expanded their girth rapidly, as the younger trees have.

An uneven-aged forest will have older trees forming the canopy, seedlings and saplings at ground level, and trees of an intermediate age in the midstory. If we return to our discussion of forest structure from Chapter 2, the dense forest structure described there—dense in both the horizontal and vertical dimensions—is the mark of an uneven-aged forest. It comes about because the forest has had the time to develop new generations of trees while some of the older trees stayed in place. It has a more natural feel, which makes sense because in the absence of major disturbance—either natural or human—forests naturally move to an uneven-aged condition. The forest that was in place when Europeans arrived was uneven-aged.

THE GREAT DEBATE

When I introduced the distinction between even-aged versus uneven-aged forests, I said it seems fairly straightforward. In reality, things might not be what they seem. In forestry circles, debates rage about how to map stands of trees within a forest. The discussion is particularly important because across the region the size of the typical forest holding continues to shrink. A classification system that makes sense on a scale of thousands of acres can fall apart when it's applied to dozens of acres.

Most of the forests of the Northeast had their origins as even-aged, which is not to say that the forest is the same age across the landscape. Each of the even-aged forests came about through its own set of circumstances. In any town, one farm field might have been abandoned in 1910, another one in 1928, a third in 1947, and a fourth in 1974. Some stands blew down in the hurricane of 1938, others were stripped before the owner put the land on the market in the 1960s and 70s.

In each of these situations, it took 20 years or so for the site to be fully occupied by a single age class of trees. Each of the resulting forests is even-aged, but when combined into a whole, they make up a composite forest that is clearly uneven-aged. You'd cause little argument with this statement. Lump it all together, and it's uneven; split it into parts, and the parts are even. But bring this broad example down to a much smaller scale and the opinions will diverge dramatically.

Let's say you own a 100-acre forest that's growing on pasture abandoned in 1940. It's clearly an even-aged forest, but 20 acres seeded in to white pine and 80 to northern hardwoods. So you have two even-aged stands. In the interest of creating habitat for different animals, you make a 5-acre patch cut in the hardwood stand. The seedlings that appear in the 5-acre patch cut represent a second age within the even-aged stand. What if every five years you were to patch cut another five acres? At what point would this stand stop being even-aged?

Remember our definition of a stand: a sub-unit of a forest whose uniformity either in species, age, or other characteristic means it can be considered one. If these patches were to be mapped as separate stands, you would continue to have the bulk of the forest in an older even-aged stand with islands of younger even-aged patches. The logical conclusion if you (and your heirs and assigns, for it would take 80 years) were to play this out for a full 16 cuts is that you would have either 16 small even-aged stands (yes, it seems ludicrous at this scale) or an uneven-aged stand. Can a patchwork of small even-aged stands of disparate ages be termed an uneven-aged stand? Or is it something different entirely?

A cookie-cutter forest like this with its 5-acre patches would never happen. Nobody—not even the most rigid forest statistician—would manage an 80-acre hardwood stand (plus 20 acres of pine) this way, except maybe on paper, yet there are real-life examples that approximate this pattern everywhere. The 100-acre forest might instead have changed hands three times since the cattle were sold in 1940. Each subsequent owner found some value to remove from the land. The first owner might have started cutting 5 cords of firewood a year from it as soon as the trees reached 6-inch diameters. The next owner was more entrepreneurial, so he cut and sold 40 cords of firewood a year. Some of the white pine trees reached 20-inch diameters at 45 years, so he cut all the big trees. He also decided he'd like to raise cattle, so he cleared 10 acres of hardwoods for pasture. The third owner let the pasture grow back to trees again, so that's a stand of young poles today. And toward the end of his tenure, he was able to have a timber sale in the older hardwoods where he cut the biggest hardwoods when they were 65 years old.

If you bought this 100 acres today, you would be buying a parcel that started as an even-aged forest but that now exhibits distinct patchiness, depending on how heavily it was cut in any one area. Forests with a similar history are common across the Northeast. At this point, much forestland has changed hands several times since it regenerated after farm abandonment, since the even-aged forest began. Owners have always had different needs and reasons for owning forestland, which affects what happens on the land. Traditionally, the woodlot has been seen as a bank account from which to draw when necessary. This is not a recipe for good forestry, but it has long been the most common practice. The extent of the cutting often has been based on the extent of the need, and only the trees large enough to have value were taken. In this way, some sections of the forest are bypassed because the trees lack commercial value.

This same sort of patchiness can result from farmland being abandoned in stages. The distant hill pasture reverts first because it's too much trouble to maintain the fences. Then, the chronically wet section of the hayfield reverts, followed by another pasture, until 25 years later, none of the land is hayed or used as pasture. This results in a forest that contains patches of even-aged stands within a broader uneven-aged structure. Each of these forests is a microcosm of the entire Northeast forest: lump it all together, and it's uneven; split it into parts, and it's even.

In the face of this reality, many foresters today are abandoning the designations of even-aged versus uneven-aged, and refer to these stands marked by patchiness as hybrid stands or mosaic stands. It's possible that this describes conditions in your family forest.

SILVICULTURAL SYSTEMS

Thus far, I've been describing the set of conditions that gave rise to the existing forests, and designating them as even-aged and uneven-aged. That distinction was the source of two corresponding silvicultural systems, also named even-aged and uneven-aged.

There are two important goals in silviculture, whether you're employing the even- or the uneven-aged system. First is to create a set of conditions in which trees can grow to their best advantage; foresters strive to give each species an opportunity to attain the size and form that brings the highest commercial value. Second is to make sure that replacement trees of desirable species are growing on the site. Succinctly, the two goals are production and regeneration.

Here's how it works. In even-aged management, there is a defined end in sight. The stand had a beginning, and it will have an end. The length of time that the trees are in place is called the rotation age. As practiced in the Northeast, a rotation typically lasts from 50 to 120 years, depending on the tree species. Along the way, there are a number of timber harvests called thinnings, which remove the poorly formed or at-risk trees in order to devote the growing space to the more promising stems. This is what we did above when we were growing the perfect sugar maple.

A thinning is an intermediate harvest, one that removes trees to provide growing space for the residual stand but is not designed to bring forth the next generation of trees. That task is left to the clearcut, seed tree, and shelterwood methods, which are known as regeneration harvests.

The difference among these three regeneration techniques is the intensity of the harvest. A clearcut removes all trees at once, while the shelterwood and seed tree methods remove fewer, and in stages. All of these happen at the end of the rotation. A forester chooses one method over the others depending on the site conditions, the species involved, what he hopes to accomplish, and what is acceptable visually to the landowner.

Shelterwood involves a cutting that removes anywhere from 40 to 60 percent of the trees, including canopy trees. A seed tree harvest differs mainly in that fewer trees (the seed trees) are left in place. These cuts allow enough light to reach the forest floor to encourage the establishment of new seedlings. The harvesting can be designed to cause soil disturbance to create a seed bed appropriate for seeds of white pine or other species that seed best on disturbed soils. A shelterwood cut also shelters the seedlings and sprouts from wind, temperature extremes, and too much sun as they grow into saplings and begin to take over the site. Several years pass before the final cut that removes the remaining mature trees, and this final harvest may even be done in stages. The length of time and the number of cuts depends on how well the regenerating species grow in the altered light conditions. Some species do best with an extended period under a light canopy.

Foresters tweak the details of their use of shelterwood to favor the species they want to regenerate. Disregarding all other variables (such as presence or absence of seeds), less residual stocking provides more light and gives a better chance to establish intermediately tolerant species like white ash and black cherry. Retaining more canopy favors shade tolerant species like sugar maple and American beech. A clearcut, on the other hand, removes all the trees down to a 1-inch or 2-inch diameter all at once. When fast-growing pioneer species are desired, or if the established regeneration suits the forester's purpose, the clearcut may provide optimal conditions.

UNEVEN-AGED MANAGEMENT

In uneven-aged management, it's quite a different process. The forest has continuous cover and is continuously regenerating, and every harvest is a regeneration harvest and an intermediate harvest. All cutting is

Figure 6.8 In a shelterwood cut, 40 to 60 percent of the trees are retained, providing shelter to the regenerating trees below.

done either as single tree or group selection. The terms themselves seem self-explanatory, but, as always, the devil is in the details. In conventional silvicultural theory, the "group" in group selection may range in size from two trees up to 2 acres. It can mean that every tree in the group larger than 2 inches in diameter is cut, or it can mean that only overstory trees are cut.

Normally, there is a target diameter to which the oldest trees of each species are grown. Yellow birch might be grown to a 24-inch diameter on a good site, while on the same site paper birch would be considered mature at 16 inches. (On a poorer site, the target for paper birch might be only 12 inches.) There is also a planned interval (known as the "cutting cycle") between entries into the stand, and these periodic harvests tend to be more frequent but less intensive than in even-aged management. Individual tree and group tree harvests are done at the same time, with individual trees being cut in the areas between the groups. Trees of all diameters are taken in each harvest.

Uneven-aged management can be very successful at regenerating shade-tolerant species, which by their nature are capable of remaining a significant part of a mature forest. If you have a valuable tolerant species in your woods, then it makes sense to favor it. In the northern hardwoods mix, sugar maple is tolerant and valuable. American beech is tolerant but its logs are worth little today. In a mixedwood forest, spruce is both tolerant and valuable. Spruce and sugar maple can be grown well in an uneven-aged system with single tree and small group selections.

It's not automatic, however, that the regenerated species will be the valuable ones. It's crucial to pay close attention to the species that are regenerating in the low light conditions, because you could instead regenerate a forest full of hophornbeam. The turkeys will be grateful for the steady supply of seeds and you'll enjoy all-night burns in your woodstove if you harvest some firewood, but your bank account won't benefit.

In the presence of large populations of white-tailed deer—which is standard in many parts of the Northeast—it may be difficult to regenerate sugar maple, red oak, or white ash because they fit the deer's very strong browsing preferences. In this case, cutting larger groups might benefit the maple, oak, and ash by "flooding" a larger area with seedlings so that some will successfully make their way above deer browsing height.

As practiced in family forests, the typical size of group selections has been a half acre or smaller. Many landowners are not comfortable with larger gaps in their canopy. Technically, the upper limit for group size is 2 acres, according to U.S. Forest Service researchers, as long as these openings are not mapped as their own stand and continue to be inventoried as part of a larger stand. For owners of larger holdings, where financial performance is a serious consideration, half-acre openings are a minimum and 2-acre groups are common.

Groups sized at 1 to 2 acres promote the regeneration of intermediate species, including some of significant commercial value, such as white ash, yellow birch,

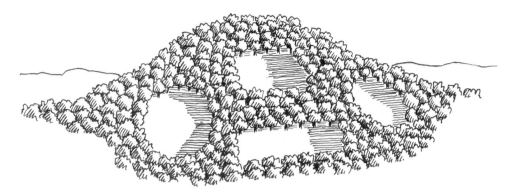

Figure 6.9   These four openings will favor slightly different mixes of regenerating trees. The less shade, the more opportunity there is for intolerant or intermediate species to get started.

and red oak. Intolerant species like paper birch and aspen might also find their way into the mix.

The shape of the opening will also influence what species will get a toehold. A cut of the same area can have either a little or a lot of edge, and edge generates shade. A cut shaped like a circle has the least edge. Circles and squares that are large enough will allow a mix of species. Shade-intolerant species such as paper birch and cherry will find favorable conditions in the center, while the edges will favor tolerant species such as sugar maple, eastern hemlock, and American beech. The increase in edge—and thus shade—in the rectangular or oblong cut would tend to favor regeneration of tolerant species.

REALITY INTRUDES

Which is the better system for you?

Uneven-aged management comes with a set of challenges, including the need for more trails to provide periodic access to all parts of the stand. Unless the trail network is planned carefully, too much of the forest can be given over to roads. Also, frequent light harvests require talented loggers who are diligent about not damaging residual stands and the regeneration that has been so hard won. Cutting larger groups makes it easier for loggers to operate and minimize damage. Since the system requires that trees of different sizes are cut in each harvest, finding markets for the various products is always a big challenge. It may also mean cutting some trees before they have reached economic maturity.

Perhaps foremost among the challenges is the requirement for more frequent timber cruises. These are needed because it's important to maintain a balance among the various size classes. Not only does the forester monitor the residual basal area (as in even-aged) but also the distribution of size classes. (See sidebar, *What's Your Q?* on page 109.) Doing so means regular data collection and recalculation of a forest's q-factor, which is a mathematical formula for determining the relative distribution of tree diameters.

Most foresters can walk into an even-aged stand and tell whether the stand is overstocked, understocked, or just right. They can even make a decent guess at the basal area and be within a reasonable margin of error. However, the forest's q-factor is not so readily apparent. Determining the relative distribution of size classes across an uneven-aged stand can only come from collecting data, and that adds expense.

It would not be unreasonable or cynical to ask whether any foresters beyond those working in research forests are practicing textbook uneven-aged management. Most foresters will acknowledge they are not.

So does that mean that even-aged management might be the better choice?

Probably not. Traditional even-aged management has its own significant drawback for many family forest owners because it requires that there will be an end of the rotation, at which point the large trees that form the canopy will be removed. Particularly for people whose forest surrounds their house, a clearcut or even a three-stage shelterwood isn't a realistic option. Removing the canopy, no matter how gently, is an intrusion into their more passive uses of the forest.

Even-aged management has its Achilles heel of the requisite final cut. Uneven-aged management eliminates that problem but has its own shortcomings, most notably that it's not financially feasible to practice it as designed.

This means that the two doctrinal systems of silviculture don't match up well with the needs of today's family forest owner. That probably shouldn't come as a surprise because the two systems were designed to produce a sustained yield of forest products from forests of significant acreage. Springing from an agrarian view of the forest as a steady source of products, these traditional silvicultural systems make sense for those owners who are looking for a competitive rate of return from their investment in forestland. They make less sense for owners looking to have a more natural forest that serves their own personal purposes, even if those purposes include making money from selling timber.

Other differences between corporate owners and family forest owners stem from the inherent limitations of the holding itself. The average family forest is not large enough to provide positive cash flow. Fixed costs are spread over too-few acres, and small holdings don't support annual harvests, so income is sporadic.

Exceptions certainly exist, but most family forests start with a set of conditions that have come about in the absence of silviculture. They're likely to be hybrid or mosaic forests, not neatly fitting into the even- or uneven-aged condition. Their best trees may have been taken in earlier harvests. The remedy for such a forest in industrial ownership might be to start over immediately. In the family forest, the best remedy probably would be to work with what you have.

In spite of those conditions, most family forest owners have a significant attachment to their land. They don't view it as

what's your q?

The forestry world, like any field of science, has arcane terms, measurements, and calculations.

One of the more arcane terms in forestry is the q-factor, a mathematical expression for the distribution of tree sizes in an uneven-aged stand.

In broad terms, uneven-aged management produces a stand with a lot of small trees and progressively fewer trees as you move up the size scale. Comparing the graphs of tree size distribution in a typical even-aged and a typical uneven-aged situation should help clarify this. In the even-aged graph, the bell-shaped curve shows quite a clump of species of more or less one age, whereas in the uneven, it's a reverse j curve, showing many small stems and few large stems.

The ratio of sizes of trees is referred to as the q-factor. It is calculated as follows. Let's say you have 9 trees per acre at 20 inches and 12 trees per acre at the next lowest slot, 18 inches. You calculate the q by dividing 12 by 9, for a result of 1.3.

If on the other hand, there were 7 trees in the 20-inch category and the same 12 trees in the 18-inch class, the q would be 12 divided by 7, or 1.7. These ratios are determined all the way down to 4 inches and up to the maximum target diameter. The overall q for the stand comes as an average of all of these steps. ⊙

Even-aged tree distribution		Uneven-aged tree distribution	
Diameter	Stems per acre	Diameter	Stems per acre
4	12	4	73
6	26	6	56
8	37	8	43
10	70	10	33
12	75	12	26
14	58	14	20
16	24	16	15
18	16	18	12
20	6	20	9
22	0	22	5

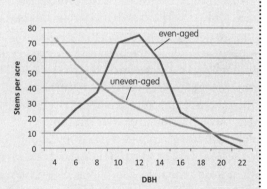

Figure 6.10   This table and graph show the distribution of tree diameters in an even-aged stand and an uneven-aged stand.

degraded, they view it as home. Because it's smaller than industrial land, everything on it is magnified. Many owners are personally connected with the land, so certain places in the forest take on special significance. An anomalous hemlock grove with a special ambience can become sacred, and a hilltop picnic area can be deemed off limits to the changes wrought by harvesting.

SILVICULTURE FOR
FAMILY FORESTS

Acknowledging that managing family forests is different from managing larger holdings, foresters have been experimenting with variations on the traditional systems. Most family forest owners want to have a forest that feels and looks like a natural forest, complete with large trees, so the general trend is toward uneven-aged or mosaic forests. The need for a predetermined balance of age classes has been largely abandoned. Given that it would be difficult to find a natural example of a balanced uneven-aged forest, this matches well with a trend toward managing for a more natural forest.

This means paying attention to natural disturbance. Most forests in the Northeast have evolved with disturbances that kill a single tree or a small group, in the case of wind or ice. On average, natural mortality might take 1 percent of the trees each year. Most gaps created by the natural disturbances are relatively small, up to a half-acre. An individual tree that succumbs in place will leave a gap in the canopy equal to the size of its crown. On the other hand, when a dominant tree is blown down, it takes others with it and creates a larger opening. Using the tree's height as the radius of a circle, an 80-foot-tall tree would make a circular opening of 20,000 square feet or just under half an acre.

Harvesting trees in patterns that mimic the forest's natural disturbance regime is at the heart of today's ecologically based forestry; foresters are prescribing harvests that approximate frequent disturbances of relatively low severity. If a forest already has multiple age classes, then an unbalanced uneven-aged management system might be employed. Harvests will entail cutting single trees or small groups. A harvest every year is unrealistic, so foresters might suggest a cutting cycle of every 10 years. In that harvest, they might aim to take 10 years' worth of "disturbance," so 10 times 1 percent of the forest, or 10 percent. Their choices of what to take and what to leave are based on the same principles as in traditional systems: create a set of conditions that grows trees well and regenerates the desired species. Over time, this unbalanced uneven-aged approach will produce a multiple-aged forest with many different cohorts.

What if the stand is even-aged? Foresters are employing variations on even-aged systems to convert even-aged stands to multiple-aged stands. One of the systems is known as an irregular shelterwood. What's not regular about it is that the shelterwood harvest doesn't take place over the entire stand at once. Nor does it remove all of the sheltering trees in a subsequent harvest at a prescribed time, because the primary goal is not to regenerate a new forest but to convert it to an uneven-aged condition. And some large trees most likely will be retained as legacy trees through old age and death.

There are different ways of going about this conversion to an uneven-aged forest. One approach is known as "expanding gap irregular shelterwood." The initial harvest in this system would involve shelterwood harvests in several groups, and the cutting in them might leave 60 percent of the canopy trees to provide shelter for the regeneration. Successive harvests are adjacent to the initial groups, and serve to expand them. At some point, the new groups will have expanded far enough to butt up against the others.

Each cut will change the light conditions beneath the canopy enough to allow a new cohort of trees to establish itself or to release advanced regeneration. The more light, the greater the chance that the full range of shade-tolerant, intermediate, and intolerant species will be present.

The answer to the question "What are you trying to accomplish with cutting?" has more permutations for a family forest owner than it does for a TIMO. How large an opening is acceptable? And for what purpose is it being opened up? All this requires a system—and a forester to implement it—that is more flexible. But that doesn't mean ignoring the tenets of silviculture.

The principles that we described at the beginning of this chapter still hold: we're looking for good results in both production and regeneration. On the production side, the way trees grow best is with adequate competition while they're putting on height. Once they've achieved that height, their crowns need to have room to expand. And for regeneration, the forester is using his skills and experience to ensure that the next trees will be those of commercially valuable species that are well-suited to the physical conditions of the site.

The goal in the unbalanced uneven-aged system is not to produce an ideal artificial distribution of age classes on every single acre; it doesn't occur that way in a natural forest, either. Instead, the goal is to grow well-formed trees of multiple ages at the appropriate density so they can continue to put on additional wood.

If the irregular shelterwood—or any of its variants—is the choice, the principle still holds. The stand is opened up enough to enable the regeneration of the next forest. The canopy, however, will never be removed all at once. Because it doesn't have a defined series of cuts, irregular shelterwood allows somebody to work with finer texture and adapt the cutting accordingly. The forest that results will have a more complex structure, one that has the characteristics of an uneven-aged or a mosaic forest.

Yes, it's a challenge. Working with a forest is not like working with a circuit board or a piece of steel. It requires a capacity to observe, respond to, and predict the actions of a natural system. These silvicultural systems—the traditional and the still-evolving variants—are our best attempts at doing so.

Forestry has been defined as the art and science of growing trees. I like that definition because it acknowledges that science never provides all the answers. And it suggests that there is an art to applying the science we do know. ▣

CHAPTER 7

APPROACHES TO MANAGEMENT

Landowners have disparate needs and interests, and want different things from their woods. To get started managing your forest, you need to identify what you want from it. It's possible to have one focus in one stand, and a different focus in another. There are many approaches to forest management you might take, but five of them stand out. In this chapter I'll go into some depth on these five:

- Natural diversity
- Sawlogs and veneer
- Firewood
- Wildlife in general
- Birds in particular

Whatever our focus in forest management, all of our choices have consequences beyond the decision to cut a certain set of trees for whatever reason we're cutting them. Being aware of this shouldn't paralyze us, but it should serve notice that all actions have further implications.

For instance, by managing a forest for sawlogs and veneer, we are also managing—whether by design or inadvertently—the animals that live there. Our forests in the Northeast are home to upwards of 300 species of birds, more than 60 mam-

mals, and close to 60 reptiles and amphibians. Add to that thousands of insects and other invertebrates, and countless microorganisms. These animals all depend on a particular set of conditions—especially the vegetation—that they've evolved to live with.

So it's really a system that we're managing. The plants and animals participate in a web of life that is predictable only in its generalities, not in its particulars. Part of the unpredictability comes courtesy of the march of time: plants and trees grow, and those changes—so subtle to our eyes—are enough to attract animals or dissuade them from sticking around. A combination of leafy structures that is good this year or this decade for one warbler species will one day lose its suitability. That vacated niche will then prove just right for another specialist.

Forest management has been evolving to give greater consideration to this ecological perspective. The long-held concept of sustained yield of wood has given way to the concept of sustainability of the system.

An ecological focus matches up particularly well with the expectations and interests of many new owners of family forests. Most forest landowners in the Northeast have more interest in their land as a place for recreation and seeing wildlife than for its timber potential. It's not that the new landowners are necessarily opposed to logging, but they are more open to chainsaws and skidders if the work results in improved habitat for wildlife and trails for recreation while also generating some periodic income.

Nearly every owner of a family forest would like to see more animals—or at least signs of their presence—on their land. One of the most satisfying aspects of forest management is that you can simultaneously improve your land's capacity to attract wildlife, increase its long-term timber value, and earn periodic income from selling wood. In this regard, you can have your cake and eat it, too.

Any management activity we undertake results in habitat change, either through careful planning or unintentionally. Changes that improve conditions for some species will reduce the suitability for others. On the macro scale, think back to the Northeast before European settlement. The vast expanses of forest favored woodland-dwelling species. Grassland birds such as bobolinks and bluebirds existed only in remotely scattered patches of open land. Early successional forests were in short supply and mostly in patches established by natural disturbances such as wind, ice, or fire. This was the natural condition, and it limited populations of chestnut-sided warblers and common yellowthroats, for instance, which thrive in very young stands.

Then, in the process of clearing the land for agriculture, we made wholesale changes to the landscape that favored a different set of animals: those that thrive in open land and edge. Woodland-dependent animals declined; amazingly, white-tailed deer nearly disappeared, and wolves and mountain lions were extirpated, partly from changes in habitat and loss of a prey base and partly from our unwillingness to live with them. Later still, as agriculture moved west and many northeastern farms were abandoned, early-successional forests abounded, which improved conditions for birds of young forests. In those conditions, ruffed grouse were incredibly plentiful.

The same thing happens on the micro scale. An unbroken canopy of mature hardwoods favors certain species; a hole in the canopy made by removing a single tree creates some change in the forest structure but less than a 3-acre patch cut would. Whether subtle or more pronounced, any change in the forest results in a change in the animals that find its conditions hospitable.

NATURAL DIVERSITY

The broadest goal a landowner could have for the forest is to preserve or enhance its natural diversity so that it's hospitable to the widest range of plant and animal species that the land can sustain. Just because it's a broad goal doesn't mean it's vague. In Chapter 4, I made the case that a fully functioning forest is the most important product we can seek. Maintaining a forest's natural diversity is closely related to this.

In the last chapter, we discussed the difference between an even-aged and an uneven-aged forest. By its very nature, an uneven-aged forest has more diversity because of its more complex structure. It has more vertical layers since more of the space between the ground and the canopy contains vegetation. It has more horizontal diversity, too, because the size and density of trees varies considerably across the forest. Dense patches of small trees are adjacent to larger trees spaced more widely. Uneven-aged forests are inherently patchy, as are the mosaic stands that have evolved as forest owners have harvested trees at different intensities.

If your forest is already in an uneven-aged or mosaic condition, you only need to encourage that through periodic harvests designed to enhance the patchiness. Identify places where you can remove mature or poorly formed trees in small groups. Harvesting these will provide a flush of green growth to the understory while improving the prospects for the large trees you retain.

If your forest is even-aged, and you want to convert it to uneven-aged to begin adding diversity, you might use the irregular shelterwood system described in Chapter 6. This system works well in northern hardwoods and mixedwood stands. Softwood plantations or pure stands of spruce-fir are more difficult to convert because opening up patches might make the newly exposed adjacent trees susceptible to windthrow.

There are also ways to increase diversity in your even-aged stand without making the conversion to uneven-aged. The big challenge will be increasing vertical diversity because a rotation of 100 years just doesn't allow enough time to establish a midstory through thinning operations. Thinning may bring about some regeneration of tolerant species, but they are most likely to bide their time in the understory. Horizontal diversity, however, can be more readily enhanced. One good way is to make a patch cut, which is a small clearcut of a half-acre to 5 acres in size. This can be particularly useful in areas where timber quality is low; by cutting all the trees in a small area, you start over and create a dense thicket of new trees. In proximity to thinned stands, these patch-cut stands will increase diversity. They function much like the group selections in uneven forests and will promote the patchiness.

These timber harvests will produce some firewood or other low-grade wood. Even though the patch cut may have been done in an area with poorly formed trees, there might be a load of sawlogs to augment the many truckloads of low-grade wood. Not only have you succeeded in increasing structural diversity, you have generated some revenue to cover the costs of making the improvements.

SAWLOGS AND VENEER

As we've discussed in earlier chapters, sawlogs have significantly greater economic value than low-grade pulpwood, firewood, and woody biomass, and prices paid for veneer far exceed those for sawlogs. If your goal is to manage your woods for high-value sawlogs and veneer, the traditional even-aged and uneven-aged systems described in the preceding chapter might be the best systems to do this.

Before we discuss another option for managing for high-value trees, let's take a step back and look at the principles behind managing for commercial value.

By focusing the growth potential of the site on the trees with the highest potential for value, we accomplish the following:

- Well-formed trees grow and add wood volume, thus increasing value.
- As trees reach certain diameter thresholds, they make jumps in value per board foot because they reach a higher grade.
- Trees reach a target size in a shorter time.
- Income is produced through any commercial harvest, such as a thinning in an even-aged system. In essence, you remove the "weeds" and someone buys them from you. How great is that?

These benefits come from either of the stand-wide silvicultural treatments we've discussed—thinning in even-aged and single tree and group selection in uneven-aged. A more intensive variation of even-aged silviculture, known as crop-tree release, might work well for you if you have at least one stand that shows real promise. The accomplishments are intensified, as is the focus of the work.

Chances are you have at least some trees that are on their way to being high-quality sawlogs or veneer trees. The further along they are in reaching this potential, the more obvious they will be. The 18-inch black cherry that's straight as a gun barrel will doubtless catch your eye or that of your forester. Or maybe there's a large red

oak whose bark is so tight it looks as if it's growing right out of its skin. If the site conditions are so good they produce these eye-catchers, then they're right for other trees of the same species, or perhaps associated species. Cast a wider net and search the immediate area for other trees with good potential. See if there are 50 potential crop trees in the acre. They might not all be perfect, but if they have the potential for sawlogs, it's worth making the effort involved in crop-tree release.

It makes great sense to devote your management efforts to the best sites. Identify the areas where your trees have the greatest potential and concentrate your crop-tree release activities there. In the other areas, you could take the more traditional stand-based approach, and do just fine. On good sites growing trees that are already showing promising form, you can achieve significant returns on an investment in time because you are deciding which trees get to stay and absorb the site's riches. By removing competing trees, you are devoting most of the site's resources (sunlight, water, soil nutrients) to the trees that have significant potential for economic return. Nature will grow 75 hardwood trees per acre to a very large size, but nature's choices have nothing to do with financial return. If you make the choice of which trees stay, you can bring those valuable trees to financial maturity faster than nature would, and you can do so without compromising the site's natural system.

You may have a stand of 10- to 12-inch hardwoods—white ash, yellow birch, sugar maple—that all got started at about the same time. By virtue of that competition, they have long ago lost their lower branches and are producing clear wood for the first 15 or 20 feet of trunk. In a stand like this, identify your 50 crop trees per acre and mark them with flagging. You then give these crop trees room to grow by implementing a crown-touching release, which means you remove any tree whose crown is touching the crop tree's crown. Only the trees directly competing are removed; the others stay, which is one way this differs from a stand-wide B-line thinning.

A more significant difference is that a B-line thinning would at best free up a tree's crown on one or two sides. Studies show that trees put on more growth when their crowns are free to grow on all four sides. In one U.S. Forest Service study plot (a 54-year-old red oak stand), unreleased trees added 1.75 inches in 10 years. Trees released on two sides gained 2.75 inches, while those released on all four sides grew

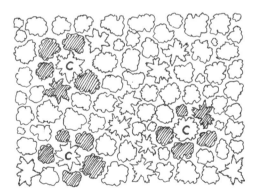

Figure 7.1   This illustration shows how a crown-touching crop tree release is accomplished. The shaded trees touching the crowns of the crop trees (marked by a C) will be cut to provide more room for the crop trees. No other trees will be removed.

4 inches in 10 years. So a crown-touching release can improve on nature by 2.25 inches per decade. An 8-inch DBH tree that would take 68.5 years to reach a target diameter of 20 inches without any treatment could reach the target in 43.6 years with the two sides released (equivalent of B-line thinning) and in 30 years with the four sides released.

Healthy crowns of immature hardwoods spread outward at the rate of about a foot per year according to U.S. Forest Service research, so the growing space between nearby crowns decreases by about 2 feet per year. If your release frees up a crown by 15 feet on all sides, the tree will have seven or eight years of freedom to expand. A second release will have additional benefits, but an interval of 10 years is recommended before the second release.

Crop-tree release has been proven to work with trees of any size, but don't start too soon with your program. The trees should be at least pole-sized, with stems greater than 5 inches DBH. That's where you can have the most dramatic impact on your forest's value, working in a pole-sized stand. The reason is in the numbers. In a natural process, most of the co-dominant trees in a pole-sized stand are not going to make it to old age—only a certain number of them will stay in the canopy. Crop-tree release allows you to make the choice of which make it to the next round. There's no guarantee, of course, that your chosen tree won't succumb to wind, insect defoliation, lightning, or any of the other causes of individual tree death, but you can increase the odds of its survival by choosing carefully. Look first at the dominant trees. They've proven their capacity to grow well; if they have good form, all the better. The co-dominant trees will benefit most from a release because you are giving them an opportunity they would otherwise have had to compete for. Look for these qualities when choosing crop trees:

- At least 25 feet tall
- Full, deep, healthy-looking crown, with few or no dead branches in the upper crown
- Trees with U-shaped forks as opposed to V-shaped
- Nicely formed butt log
- No epicormic branching
- High-value species. We're looking for commercial value here, so don't bother with noncommercial species. This is not to say that you couldn't use a broader definition for crop trees and favor a perfectly formed hophornbeam, striped maple, or quaking aspen.

In a stand of pole-sized trees like this, nothing will be sold—it's strictly a precommercial operation. You (or a logger paid to do this) would fell the adjacent trees and leave them on the forest floor. If some of the trees are not easy to fell, they can be girdled instead—a technique in which two parallel rings are cut into the tree's circumference to disrupt the flow of water, nutrients, carbohydrates, and hormones. In this way, the girdled trees are removed as competition and they die on the stump, losing limbs and branches from the crown over time and eventually falling over.

When crop-tree release is done in a stand with larger trees, there will likely be some opportunities for revenue. Most of the trees would be sold for firewood, though it's quite possible that some would have enough quality that they could be sold for sawlogs.

It's hard to imagine a 100-acre family forest blessed with uniformly rich growing sites. More likely, it will have pockets of promise. Consequently, crop-tree release is not a practical approach across an entire stand. Find your best sites, and invest your energy there.

If you have been trained to operate a chainsaw safely, a crop-tree release project is a very rewarding process. I speak from experience when I say that it's tremendously satisfying to choose the trees and mark them, fell or girdle the competition, and best of all keep track of your progress by measuring DBH at regular intervals. You might find yourself taking issue with the adage that money doesn't grow on trees.

RANGE OF BENEFITS

In growing trees for commercial value, either through stand-wide prescriptions or crop-tree release, the harvesting of the primary products is deferred, their value increasing over time because they have more growing space. Immediate byproducts occur, however, in the form of wood products and habitat changes. These treatments remove marketable trees, most of them of low value, but depending on the quality of the stand, the treatments probably will generate some sawlogs, too.

In each case, crop-tree release or a stand-wide intermediate treatment, there will be a number of changes to the habitat the site offers. These harvests open the canopy, so more sun reaches the forest floor and any saplings and shrubs growing there. If none of these are present, they can now develop from seed sources that have been waiting in the leaf litter for this opportunity to grow. On the opposite side of the ledger, any invasive species already in the understory will be given an opportunity to flourish. Care must be taken not to provide optimal conditions for their spread.

On a more long-term basis, if the canopy is opened up significantly, the saplings will have an opportunity to develop into the midrange, increasing the complexity of the forest structure. As we discussed earlier, greater diversity of horizontal and vertical structure provides opportunities for increased breadth of species. More of the three-dimensional block from ground to canopy is being used by wildlife.

If some trees are girdled, these standing snags can serve as valuable perches for raptors and can be excavated by woodpeckers for their own use or later use by any of the many species of cavity nesters, including flying squirrels and nuthatches. In any harvest, it's a good idea to leave at least six standing snags per acre for this purpose. Over time, the snags' limbs, branches, and trunks will end up horizontal on the forest floor, providing coarse woody debris for many users. The fallen matter provides ground-level structure and habitat for small mammals, reptiles, and amphibians. In turn, these creatures become prey for raptors or other predators. And as the wood begins to decompose, it provides food for any number of organisms.

FIREWOOD

The woodlot has a long, continuous presence in the history of land use in the Northeast. Even as early farmers were clearing as much land as possible for growing crops and raising animals, most of them kept some land in woods to provide the fuel to heat the house and cook the food. Often the woodlot was land too wet or too steep to grow food but adequate for growing firewood. Before insulation and efficient woodstoves, the fuel demands of a porous farmhouse with a fireplace were remarkably high. Twenty cords of wood per farmstead is not an unreasonable estimate of typical wood usage.

It would be hard today to find people who burn anywhere near that amount, and with well-insulated houses and more efficient woodstoves and furnaces, typical home consumption is now in the range of four cords or less.

If your primary goal for your family forest is to cut four cords of firewood a year, how would you go about it? Firewood comes along as a byproduct in any harvest, so it's a natural secondary goal associated with timber management for valuable sawlogs.

If you want to manage primarily for firewood, however, you can build on the knowledge of what makes a good sawlog, because you want to avoid cutting those trees. You also want to avoid compromising their future by damaging them as you fell trees or by opening up the woods too much around them. Even if you don't envision a timber sale, it's still better to not damage whatever well-formed trees you have. They add to the value of the woodlot when the time comes for you to sell it or pass it along to heirs.

The first consideration then is form. Firewood trees are the ones you'd remove because they have no chance of being a keeper tree. If a tree doesn't have a log in it now or the potential for one in the future, then it's a firewood tree.

Structural defects, such as narrow V-shaped forks, are a prime reason to cut a tree for firewood. The lower the narrow fork is on the bole, the less likely there's sawlog value there. Look for trees with protruding branch stubs, live limbs low on the bole, or otherwise compromised trunks.

Next to consider is any sign of disease or decay. If there is a mushroom of any kind growing on the trunk, it is feeding on rotting wood. The area of rot may or may not be extensive, but its presence shows that the potential for sawlog value is going or gone. Above and below the fungus, the wood may be sound and perfectly good for burning. Sometimes, the sign of decay or weakness is not as obvious as a hen of the woods or an artist's conk, two types of fungus that grow on the bole. Learn to recognize cankers, wounds, and cracks that will shorten the tree's life and keep it from growing sawtimber.

Then think about species. There's a hierarchy in hardwood species, based on their capacity to provide BTUs, and you'll see that some of them overlap the good lumber trees. Black locust, hophornbeam, and shagbark hickory have the highest BTUs per pound of wood, but they aren't particularly valuable outside of the firewood market. You can sell locust and hickory sawlogs, but hornbeam is purely firewood. The chart below shows the highest BTU species, but use it in the context of what you have. If you have a plentiful source of a high-BTU species, that's your target species for firewood. Don't cut your only red oak just because it burns hot. Keep in mind that you can burn low-BTU species such as white birch and aspen in the shoulder seasons—early and late winter—when you just need to take the chill out of the house. You'd then reserve your maple, beech, yellow birch, and oak for the coldest weather. Ash needs the least drying time of all hardwoods; aspen, on the other hand, never seems to dry.

Chances are you won't have any difficulty in finding plenty of candidates for

Hardwood Species by BTU	
Species	*BTUs available per cord (millions)*
Black locust	24.9
Hophornbeam	24.6
Apple	23.9
White oak	23.2
Beech	21.7
Sugar maple	21.7
Yellow birch	21.3
Red oak	21.3
White ash	21.0
Paper birch	18.7
Red maple	18.7
Black cherry	18.7
American elm	17.6

Figure 7.2 Hardwood species and the BTUs available per cord.

the woodpile. But there are still some things to consider as you make your decisions. It's best to make choices of trees to cut when you have either a paint can or a roll of surveyor's tape in hand. When you make choices with the chainsaw in hand, you might regret your selections. In one session, mark the trees to be cut; later, return with your chainsaw and take another look to confirm your original thinking. Here are a few things to keep in mind. The firewood trees should be:

- *Easy to fell.* You don't want to be damaging crop trees as you fell any tree. And you don't want the tree to get hung up on other trees on the way down. Use directional felling techniques, and plan the cut carefully. If you have any doubt that you can fell it cleanly and safely, choose another tree.

- *Accessible.* What machine are you going to use to get the wood out? If you own a tractor, then you can skid the log to a place where you can work on it. If all you have is a pickup truck, don't despair. Plenty of weekend warriors bring in their four cords of wood with a pickup. It just means that you need to cut trees close to roads you can reasonably drive on.

- *Worth the considerable effort it will take to split it into firewood.* You've been cautioned not to cut potential sawlogs; nor do you want to cut trees that are so twisted and gnarly you'll have to spend the whole day trying to turn them into firewood. Trees with that much character should probably stay standing.

The last thing to consider is whether you should cut your firewood in patches or by thinning. Depending on your secondary goals, you may want to thin stands where you have the potential for sawlogs, or cut patches where the quality is generally low. Cutting patches can make the felling easier to accomplish because it can create a hole into which you fell the next trees. All of this can be done within the bounds of any management plan.

How much to cut? If most forestland in the Northeast can be expected to grow half a cord a year per acre, is there a problem with removing more than that? There are two parts to the answer. First, if the trees are poorly formed and removing them frees up trees with better form, it makes good silvicultural sense. Many stands are overstocked with cull trees because of past high-grading, which removed all the valuable sawlogs. Second, the half-cord per acre should be considered across the entire acreage, not just on that particular acre. In other words, your annual cut shouldn't exceed the half-cord per acre as an overall average. Even if you only own 2 acres, by being judicious in your choices and removing only cull trees, you can probably cut four cords per year indefinitely. The growth gets redistributed to the other trees. If you ever get to the end of the firewood and start biting into the sawlogs, then it might be time for a timber sale. In that case, you can pay the logger to leave you four cords of log-length firewood, made up of the parts of the trees above the sawlogs.

When to cut? It's best to cut trees in winter. That way, they'll have a full year to dry out, and they'll start the drying process without any sap in them. And you'll avoid damaging the residual trees in spring and summer, when the bark is loose and the trees left standing are most prone to being skinned by errant felling. After the leaves are down, the bark tightens up, reducing the chance for damage.

One last word. If you haven't taken a chainsaw safety class recently, you should do it. There have been great advances in the techniques for directional felling. A Swedish logger, Soren Erickson, brought his training technique for safe and productive logging to the United States in the 1990s. It's known as The Game of Logging, and many organizations sponsor training sessions that teach landowners as well as loggers how to work safely in the woods using these techniques.

WILDLIFE MANAGEMENT

For many years, wildlife management meant game management. Officials at state fish and wildlife departments saw their job as managing game animals for the hunters and anglers who funded the department through license fees and excise taxes on rifles, ammunition, fishing rods, and tackle. In the past few decades, the mission of wildlife departments has shifted, a change signaled by the renaming of many departments from "Fish and Game" to "Fish and Wildlife."

Because of wildlife managers' historic focus on game animals, it is the game animals' habitat needs that have been studied most thoroughly. Volumes and volumes have been written about managing habitats for turkeys, ruffed grouse, woodcock, white-tailed deer, snowshoe hare, cottontails, migratory waterfowl, and game fish such as trout and bass. Hunting and

conservation groups like the Wild Turkey Federation, Ruffed Grouse Society, Ducks Unlimited, and Trout Unlimited have spent considerable time and money planting oak, patch-cutting to regenerate aspen stands, building duck boxes, and restoring streambanks, all in the name of providing for the needs of their favorite species.

Fortunately, though, by concentrating on the needs of game animals, managers also have been providing good habitat for many other species that share the same needs. For instance, the ruffed grouse requires thick sapling stands of hardwoods with dead logs on the ground for its breeding habitat. This same habitat serves the needs of a number of small mammals, amphibians, and songbirds, including veeries, redstarts, and rose-breasted grosbeaks.

White-tailed deer are generalists, and they can thrive under a multitude of situations, from the industrial forest to agricultural land to suburbia. As long as food is within their reach, they will find it. The one limiting factor for deer is a particularly harsh winter, which can have deadly consequences. In winters with many nights of sub-zero temperatures and deep snow lasting for extended periods, deer need to have access to deeryards, known technically as deer wintering areas. These thick softwood stands provide cover that intercepts snow, reducing its depth and making traveling through it less demanding on the deer's energy stores. The dense cover also creates a microclimate with less wind and slightly warmer temperatures.

If you have an extensive stand of softwoods on your land, you should inspect it for signs of deer use in the winter. You can

Figure 7.3   Deer congregate in deeryards to escape harsh winter conditions. *Photo by Susan C. Morse.*

also check with your state fish and wildlife department to see if your stand has been mapped as a deer wintering area. Some states regulate or have guidelines for harvests in deeryards. The effectiveness of the softwood cover varies with species, with hemlock being the best cover and pine the least beneficial.

Deeryard management has as its focus the need for long-term continuity of cover and adjacent food sources. The combination of the two is crucial. Leaving an unbroken overstory of mature spruce and fir might seem like the thing to do, but it's not the recommended management strategy. Patches with regeneration of hardwood species for food and softwoods for future cover are keys to this management.

The goal is at least 50 percent softwood canopy cover at all times.

Other animals, such as snowshoe hare, benefit from this type of cover, as do many of the birds that winter over. Aside from deeryards, no other habitat consideration needs to be given to the whitetail. We all enjoy seeing deer, but in much of the Northeast, their populations are high enough that they are compromising forest regeneration. This goes beyond being a silvicultural concern. Studies show that a shrub layer stripped clean by deer sees almost no use by songbirds.

Coyotes are another adaptable generalist, but most animals are less adaptable and have habitat requirements so specific that the loss of that particular habitat can put the species' local population in a tail-spin. The woodcock, for instance, feeds in dense young stands, nests in slightly more mature woods (15 to 30 years old), and performs its courtship ritual in open meadows. If these three elements don't exist in close proximity to one another—and the combination is becoming scarcer in the Northeast where forests are aging and former agricultural land is turning into subdivisions—woodcock will not be there. Non-game species that benefit from this same set of conditions include some whose populations have fallen alarmingly in recent years, such as the whippoorwill and golden-winged warbler.

One last species of game animal that deserves some thought is the brook trout. You might not immediately think of it as a forest animal, but whether it's living in a pond, stream, or river, it is entirely dependent on the clear, cold water that springs from the forest. To manage for brook trout, you should be thinking about shade.

Streams that run through open, shadeless land heat up rapidly in summer. Under full canopy cover, water temperatures remain in the preferred range for brook trout of 65 degrees or colder.

It's not that you have to forgo any streamside harvests forever. If you have a closed canopy over the brook, you can remove an occasional tree. Trees on or near riverbanks are often poorly formed because they tend to lean (sometimes dramatically) toward the open stream corridor. If all your buffer trees are like this, it's better to just leave them. If you happen to have a mature veneer tree growing there, however, by all means pluck it out at the next harvest. The goal is to retain a closed canopy—removing an occasional valuable tree shouldn't compromise the canopy. Its neighbors will quickly expand to fill in the canopy space.

Another virtue of the leaning trees is that some of them will eventually fall into the water. When one does, don't be tempted

Figure 7.4   A buffer strip of undisturbed ground runs adjacent to this stream. The vegetation holds the bank firm and shades the water, keeping it cold.

to free it up or drag it out of the water. It's a source of cover for trout, and its leaves and decomposing wood will feed all sorts of microorganisms and stream insects, which are the key to the health of a trout stream. It will change the flow pattern in the stream but in a natural way that does not have a negative effect. Natural processes are better river engineers than excavators, bulldozers, and trucks full of rip-rap.

Even headwater streams so small you can step right across them should have a canopy of shade. Water that flows through the openings in full sun gets heated, and an aggregation of warm feeder streams makes a warm river. And once it warms up, it only cools down when it's recharged by a soaking rain. Shade-providing buffers are beneficial for the whole riparian system.

MANAGING FOR BIRDS

We all love to see animals. They invigorate our spirit. Of all the animals, it's birds—so colorful, melodious, and often close at hand—that have a special hold on many of us. It makes perfect sense to want to enhance habitat for songbirds, but you can quickly work yourself into a lather if you try to manage your forest "for the birds." Which ones? There's the rub. We have more than 300 species of birds in the Northeast. Some of them are resident but most are part-timers here for the summer to breed. Different bird species have decidedly different tastes, and the kind of forest one species prefers will be bypassed as unsuitable by another.

Let's look at three insect eaters to illustrate this point. Picture a tree swallow glid-

ing, swooping, and making sudden dips and turns as it feeds on insects over an open meadow or a pond or large river. Tree swallows nest in open areas near water, using holes in trees excavated by woodpeckers. Our second insect eater, the brown creeper, is less showy in its feeding. A meticulous gleaner, it probes bark crevices and circles up the bole in search of insects. Its specific habitat requirement is a large dead tree with loose bark, because it attaches its nest between the trunk and the bark. Then there's the ovenbird, which constructs its nest on the ground in the leaf litter of a mature hardwood forest and finds its food there as well. Besides insects, it consumes snails, slugs, and earthworms.

Three birds, three very specific sets of conditions. Multiply that by 100, and you'll see how difficult it would be to favor our 300 breeding birds. Each bird species that nests in our region has its own ideas about what to eat, where to roost, and where to nest. They may also have specific habitat needs when caring for fledglings. You'll find that it's simultaneously both very difficult and very easy to manage for birds. Any action you undertake will enhance the habitat for one and diminish it for another. Even inaction has an effect because forests change regardless of what we do, so habitat is ephemeral. Birds fill very specific niches, and those niches are affected by the passage of time and the growth of the vegetation. It's impossible to overstate the link between birds and vegetation. The birds are there because the vegetation provides food, cover, and a nest site. Birds segment the forest and use what works for them. When an area no

recreation

*R*ecreation is a word that can describe almost every activity but doesn't fit any of them particularly well.

It can easily trivialize a pursuit that has deeper significance. Taking a walk to a special place in the woods that provides spiritual sustenance is not usually called "recreation." Diligently studying plants and understanding plant communities brings pleasure surely, but it's not a game. And for many hunters, their pursuit is much more than recreation.

Still, if we're talking about the wide variety of pursuits that people engage in not for profit but for refreshment, then recreation is probably the best word available. For many of these pursuits, trails are an asset. There's nothing more inviting than trails that pass through different types of woods and provide hikes of varying length

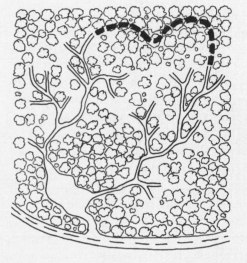

Figure 7.5   These skid trails will function as a nice trail network when the logging is done. The farthest ends of the two trails will be connected to form a loop by clearing the path marked by the dashed line.

and difficulty. Whether you're introducing a child or other newcomer to the woods or taking a walk with an elder, trails provide a sense of comfort

longer meets their needs, they'll move on and another bird might find it useful.

So what can you do for the birds? The best approach might be to simply manage for natural diversity as we discussed at the beginning of this chapter. That makes particular sense because one of the tenets of increased diversity is creating more layers in the forest structure, and that is probably the most important thing you can do for birds.

Almost all—if not all—songbirds use more than one forest layer for feeding,

roosting, breeding, nesting, and raising broods. A single bird may use the herbaceous layer, the woody understory, the subcanopy, and the overstory. A diverse forest with many trees species will benefit the whole avian entourage, but most important for birds is vertical diversity. You might think that since birds can fly, they can simply flit up or down to find what they need, but it doesn't work that way. Each bird is looking for a particular combination of circumstances. You can and security. Whether it's giving the dog its daily exercise or a quiet walk with stops for contemplation, a daily hike on a favorite trail can restore both body and mind.

To be sure, there are recreational activities that don't rely on trails. In hunting, it's crucial to venture out beyond or between trails. The same holds true for all sorts of nature study, whether your interests are birds, wildflowers, mushrooms, frogs, rocks, or medicinal plants. There's much to be discovered beyond the trail. Still, even in these pursuits, trails do come in handy, if for no other reason than to provide a convenient route home after a long session of bushwhacking. They also serve to break large areas into manageable units.

As nice as trails can be, most landowners wouldn't spend money to bring in heavy equipment to create a trail network. If you have a timber harvest, however, you can end up with trails without paying for them directly.

Any commercial harvesting operation relies on trails and roads: skid trails for bringing felled trees to the landing, and a logging road from the landing to a public road. Before the job begins, a forester or logger will flag where the new skid trails will be created.

The ideal for a trail and road network for timber harvesting would resemble a tree with a main trunk and several branches leading to it. This design can't always be achieved, but in general, there will be more than one skid trail leading to a landing, where the truck road begins. Skid trails are laid out for effective transport of logs from the forest to the landing, while making sure that their placement doesn't damage the site, especially any watercourses. During planning, it makes sense to consider the trails' later use for recreation. Having the logger connect some of the skid trails not just at the hub but at their opposite end can result in a nice loop. ⊙

do the most for birds by taking this broad approach of increasing vertical diversity.

But perhaps you want to do more, something specific. Personally, I couldn't live without the wood thrush. It sings at the softly lit edges of the day in a voice so transcendent that angels couldn't improve on it, but then ends with a funny little bzz that anchors it in its earthly realm. It sings to me, and because it does, I want to do something to keep it in my woods.

Here's the lowdown on what the wood

thrush needs: it sings from the canopy, nests about 10 feet off the ground, and feeds on or near the ground. It feeds predominantly on insects but will eat berries and other small fruits in the shrub layer. It spends time scratching in the leaf litter for insects. In summary, its habitat needs include a mature closed canopy and a well-developed shrub-sapling layer. In my woods, I can provide that combination through the single-tree or small group selection cuts of uneven-aged management. It could even be accomplished for a time in even-aged management during the thinning phase, but when the overstory is removed, the wood thrush will find another home and be replaced by those birds who need the early successional stage of a forest.

My point is that you could research the specific habitat requirements of your favorite bird and take action to meet those requirements (if possible) on your land. That will certainly provide great satisfaction when you see and hear more of your favorite bird in your woods. But there's more that you can do. If you want to help your woods come alive with birdsong of all kinds, you can keep one eye on the birds while you go about your business managing for timber, for firewood, or for biodiversity. Here's how.

The vast majority of the birds in our woods are migrants. They arrive around May and leave by October. While they are here, their program is to breed, nest, raise young, and repeat if possible. Then they need to fatten up to prepare for their long flight south.

Each species has particular needs, which can be broken down into these four elements:

- Singing perch
- Nest site
- Place to forage
- Cover from predators

As we look at our forests and take actions in them, we can pay attention to anything we might do to enhance the ways we provide any of these elements. With that in mind, let's look at the woods from the ground up.

Ground. Gravity being hard to resist, much of the wood in dead or dying trees ends up on the forest floor. There are lots of uses for downed wood, either coarse or fine, with a diameter of 4 inches as the threshold between fine and coarse. Decomposing wood is home for insects, thus providing food for birds. It can even be a perch site for some, including the ovenbird. Ruffed grouse use downed trees as drumming logs for their courtship display.

A predator is more likely to come up empty-handed if it has to sort through brush, saplings, dead logs, and the rootballs of blowdowns. Interestingly, several studies have shown that nests on the ground are less vulnerable to predators than nests in the canopy. This is one reason why logging slash is a good thing. If you collect some of it into piles, it's even better.

Rootballs are among the least appealing sights in the woods, but before you call in the heavy equipment, remind yourself that the winter wren finds tangled upturned roots perfect for hiding its nest.

From an ecological point of view, the more dead trees, dead branches, and dead leaves we can bring ourselves to leave behind when working in the woods, the better. It's fascinating how important the ground is to an animal that can leave it with one beat of its wings.

Sapling and shrub layer. We'll define this as from the ground to a height of 5 feet. Dense stems and leaves of herbaceous plants are useful but not as much as woody-stemmed plants. Many birds use this layer for foraging and for nesting. If thick, it provides good cover as they feed. These woody stems are trees and shrubs, which points out that the thick tangle is ephemeral. Before you know it, they will be pole-sized trees, and the shrub layer will be sparse. Regular firewood cutting of patches of trees can provide enough of an opening to bring in a thick patch of woody stems.

Midstory. You want to have trees and shrubs growing into and through the midstory's height of 6 to 30 feet. A whole different set of birds uses this niche for the same purposes: nest sites, protective cover, and a foraging place. The blue-headed vireo is a midlevel forager found most often in conifer forests but sometimes in hardwoods and mixedwoods. When you see lots of green not just near the ground and in the canopy, you will also be hearing more voices in the songbird chorus.

Standing snags and cavity trees. Standing dead trees provide a great opportunity for excavating woodpeckers. Aspen and white birch are favored targets of flickers and yellow-bellied sapsuckers. The cavities that sapsuckers and other woodpeckers make are then used as nest sites for many other birds and den sites for mammals. Songbirds, flying squirrels, squirrels, bats, weasels, owls, and raccoons are among the many animals that use cavity trees. As the crown dies back, dead branches and what's left of the top are used as perches and roosts. When looking for cavity trees, think also of those in the future. Prime candidates are injured trees and those with a limb broken off.

And don't wait for them to die on their own. Girdling some larger unmarketable trees when they are interfering with good quality timber trees will improve timber quality over the long haul and provide avian housing for many years. Later, on the ground, they will serve as coarse woody debris. Aim to have six or more standing dead trees per acre, and include at least one that's larger than 18 inches DBH.

Canopy. Don't think of the canopy only as the height of the tallest trees in your forest. Regenerating stands have a canopy that increases in height each year. The height of the canopy influences which birds will nest in it. Early successional birds will feel at home until the canopy exceeds 20 feet. At that point, they will look elsewhere.

The blackburnian warbler, whose gold, black, and orange coloring makes it one of the most beautiful birds in the woods, wants a high canopy. Birders get sore necks from searching for the blackburnian. Scarlet tanagers also sing from perches high in the canopy.

Canopies are measured not just in terms of their height but also in terms of how open or closed they are. Bird habitat specialists define three levels of canopy closure:

- Less than 30 percent (open)
- 30–80 percent
- More than 80 percent (closed)

We can match the canopy condition to a representative warbler with a color in its name: the chestnut-sided warbler will prefer the open, the black-throated blue warbler will prefer the middle range, and the black-throated green warbler likes a closed canopy.

The effects of canopy closure are felt down to the ground, because the more

a)

Figure 7.6 Different bird species have different preferences for canopies: *a)* The chestnut-sided warbler prefers the more open woods at the top; *b)* black-throated blue warblers prefer crown closure of 30 to 80 percent; *c)* black-throated green warblers thrive in full canopy conditions.

b)

c)

a canopy is closed, the less likely there will be an understory. One other aspect of canopies is the value of what's known as inclusions. A single conifer or a small patch of them in a hardwood forest will be used by birds for winter shelter and sometimes for nesting.

The timing of logging is influenced by several factors, but minimizing it during the bird breeding season, if feasible, will be helpful to many birds, especially those that nest on or near the ground, such as vireos, wrens, thrushes, and some sparrows. Most birds begin breeding in the heart of mud season, when logging is off limits anyway, and their offspring are safely fledged by about August 10.

All of the various management choices I've outlined in this chapter are brought about by cutting trees. In the next chapter, I'll discuss the various ways those timber harvests come about. ◘

CHAPTER 8

SUCCESSFUL TIMBER SALES

The prospect of harvesting and selling trees makes some landowners uneasy, especially those who are new to the experience of owning land. Still, nearly every management choice that we have been talking about is implemented through a timber sale. The exceptions are cutting firewood for home use and pre-commercial timber stand improvement projects; these usually have relatively low impact because heavy equipment isn't required.

Sooner or later, however, a forest owner is likely to sell timber. It can be a remarkably simple hands-off business transaction, but if you're serious about what happens on your land, you won't take a laissez-faire approach. You'll be well-served by knowing beforehand the mechanics of the process, some of the decisions that need to be made, and some of the potential pitfalls and liabilities. In addition, no state government in the Northeast is entirely absent from oversight of timber harvests, and some are more present than others, so you should make yourself familiar with the regulations in your state.

A good timber sale experience will produce an acceptable financial gain and a change in the conditions of your woods that meets your objectives. A bad timber sale experience may well sour you on the whole forest stewardship process. The stakes are high, and it's important to get it right. The challenge is compounded because it is not always immediately apparent if you've succeeded.

Trees are large organisms, growing in places that are sometimes tough to reach. The harvesting process probably won't be as tidy as many landowners would like. But not all messes are created equal. The disturbance of a harvest can promote future value growth or it can degrade it for decades. It can influence regeneration positively or negatively. It can minimize erosion or accelerate it. Which of these occurs—good or bad—is not always readily apparent to a nonprofessional. It takes a practiced eye to read the results of a harvest.

Similarly, evaluating the adequacy of the price paid and received for a given tree is not simple. When a tree is harvested, it's the culmination of a decades-long process of growth that has probably taken place under the tenures of several owners. Through the decades, the tree might have been ignored or carefully cultivated; either way, its current owner should receive

Figure 8.1 This photo was taken three summers after a timber harvest. A flush of saplings and berry bushes has grown up through the logging slash.

full and fair value. A number of variables contribute to the calculation, including market demand, the relative difficulty of logging conditions in your woods, and whether any additional work—access improvements, habitat management, restoration of problem areas, for instance—will be done in conjunction with the harvesting of timber.

It's time to provide a warning and some advice. The warning: commercial timber harvesting disturbs the land. There's no getting around it. You'll see a serious change in your woods, and it's important to come to grips with this before you begin a sale. The advice: to help ensure a good outcome, retain the services of a forester whom you have chosen with some care. A forester can help sort out the good from the bad, and explain to you the changes that are merely cosmetic and ephemeral from any that are significant and enduring. And in preparation for your own sale, an experienced forester can show you logging jobs in progress as well as some from a couple of years ago that have had the chance to green up again. Remember that logging is an ephemeral use, unlike a strip mall or housing development, which changes the land irrevocably.

Here's how a timber sale works. Let's assume that the decision about the types and sizes of trees to be harvested has already been made, guided by the management plan, or occasionally by the need to salvage trees damaged by storms. Let's also assume that a forester is overseeing the process under a fee-for-services contract with the landowner. Armed with his paint gun, the forester will spray a spot or a stripe of paint on trees at eye level and usually with a spot at ground level, perhaps on a root flare. The marked trees are the ones to be cut. The stump spot remains after a tree is cut and serves as a forester's means of ensuring that only marked trees are cut.

In certain circumstances, the forester will mark in the opposite way, known as "leave tree" marking, in which only the trees to be left are painted. This is far less common than "cut tree" marking. When patches, strips, or groups of trees are to be cut, a forester may mark the perimeter of the area rather than marking each tree within the perimeter. If a forester and logger have worked together enough, there will be occasions when the forester simply provides a set of instructions on the trees that will be kept. "Let's retain anything with the potential for a sawlog, and don't let the stocking go below 70 square feet," for example. In this case, the forester doesn't mark any trees. This is very common in large holdings, and less so in family forests.

Before any trees are cut, an owner (through his agent, the forester) must find a buyer, agree to terms, and take care of a number of details about what will take place in the woods. Trees are bought and sold under a variety of contractual and legal arrangements. A sample contract with a logger is found in the appendix.

The first decision to make is whether to sell logs or trees. If you're selling logs, you need to have the trees cut, brought to a roadside location, and converted into logs. Logs are manufactured products, and selling them can be handled in several ways. Most owners do not have the requisite equipment to produce logs ready for sale, so they typically contract with a logger to do this work and a forester to assist with marketing. For many reasons (the major one of which we will discuss in chapter 9, on the tax applied to timber sale income), selling logs is an approach generally taken only by large companies.

The more common practice is to sell trees, which is known as a stumpage sale because it's selling the tree as it stands "on the stump." This is analogous to sales of farm machinery and old cars in which the classified ad reads "where is, as is."

You can sell stumpage in one of two ways: either as a lump sum sale, or on a pay-as-cut basis, also known as mill tally, unit-priced, or mill-delivered.

LUMP-SUM SALE

In a lump-sum stumpage sale, a buyer purchases the entirety of the designated standing trees for a price determined by bid or negotiation. It is customary practice for the seller to provide an estimate of the quantity of wood in the trees, which he arrives at by tallying the volume while marking the trees to be cut.

The relative value of the particular forest's species and products determines the care and time that should be devoted to collection of tree data during timber sale preparation. It makes sense to spend more time gathering accurate information on a tree worth $200 than on one worth 25 cents.

One alternative to marking and taking measurements on every tree is to mark each tree, but measure only a small percentage. A second alternative, useful with perimeter-delineated areas and when tree selection is made from a prescription rather than individual marking, is to determine volume by a statistically based field sampling inventory method. This method produces results on a per-acre basis, which can be expanded to the timber sale area.

After the landowner's forester has developed a description of what is offered, a decision on whether to negotiate a sale or put it to bid can be made. In a negotiated sale, the forester will use his tally to arrive at an opinion of value or a minimum acceptable price. The appraisal process takes into account the following: volume and quality of timber; the difficulty of logging; the costs of roadwork, culverts, and gravel; regulatory costs; distance to market for the various products; and current market prices. Armed with the appraisal, the forester will either ask the buyer (typically, a logger or a sawmill) for an offer, or

propose a price. The buyer is free to cruise the timber to get his own estimate of the volume and its value. Having done so, he may make a counter-offer.

Following negotiation, the forester will make a recommendation to the landowner about whether to accept an offer and enter into a contract. The decision to negotiate with a particular buyer is usually driven by a few reasons: known quality of the buyer's work and established relationship with the forester; the logger's use of harvesting equipment that matches the job; availability to complete the job within a certain time frame; and the ability to pay a fair price for the particular type and quality of timber offered.

The alternative to a negotiated sale is a bid sale, which in this region is most typically done with sealed bids. One advantage of this method is that it determines unambiguously what the current value of the timber is in the marketplace. At times, the high bid may be significantly higher than the forester's appraised value, the result of a buyer who has especially good markets for the material offered, or of some unusual circumstances that make him willing to pay more than apparent current market value.

In a sealed bid sale, the landowner's forester prequalifies a list of prospective bidders, who receive a sale prospectus and are given an opportunity to view the timber for sale. The owner's forester receives sealed bids, which are opened at a time specified in the prospectus. With the advice of the forester, the owner makes a decision on whether to accept any of the bids. It is customary practice for the owner to reserve the right to reject all bids. If a bidder is selected, a contract is signed, at which point a performance bond is collected. Unsuccessful bidders are notified of the results.

A disadvantage of sealed bid sales is the possibility of the forester having to supervise an unfamiliar logging contractor. This can happen, for instance, when the winning bidder is a sawmill that contracts with an independent logger to harvest the timber. Prequalification of bidders and strong contract language are essential landowner safeguards, but they provide no absolute guarantee that problems will not arise.

There's one last item to cover in the discussion of lump-sum sales. The price paid for the stumpage is not linked to the actual yield; the buyer is paying for the specified trees. How the trees are used is entirely up to the buyer.

In sales of this nature, it's in the buyer's interest to find as much yield or value as possible out of each tree. This means there will be little saleable wood left behind. In days past, this was a selling point for many because it meant the woods were scrubbed clean of anything marketable; today, when people are encouraged to place more value on coarse woody debris for its ecological benefits, the drive to use every last bit of fiber has waned. The buyer, however, still has an incentive to use everything, so it's important that utilization details are negotiated and agreed upon. Otherwise, it can lead to a dispute.

MILL-TALLY SALE

Family forest owners are much more likely to sell timber by way of a mill-tally sale. In this form of stumpage sale, the selling price of the designated trees is determined from prices per-unit delivered to a mill or concentration yard. The prices are agreed to in a timber sale contract with the logger. The seller is paid at a certain rate/MBF (per thousand board feet) by species and often for different grades of sawlogs; at a rate per cord for firewood, and sometimes pulpwood; and at a rate per ton or cord for pulpwood or chips. The following chart shows hypothetical prices excerpted from a timber sale contract.

The logger will pay the landowner for standing trees as follows:	
Hardwood pulp/firewood	$6.00/cord
Pine pulp	$1.00/cord
Hemlock pulp	$8.00/cord
Chips	$1.00/ton

Payment for sawlogs delivered (the logger pays the trucking) will be as follows:

Mill price/MBF	Paid to landowner
Less than or equal to $150	$10
$150–200	$45
$201–250	$60
$251–300	$100
$301–350	$125
$351–400	$150
$401–450	$175
$451–500	$200
$501–600	$250
$601–1,000	60% of mill price
$1,001–2,000	70% of mill price
$2,001 and above	75% of mill price

Please note that this price schedule is hypothetical and doesn't reflect current market prices or conditions in your woodlot, which may bring negotiated prices either higher or lower than these. There's one more variation on a mill-tally sale: it's not uncommon for mills to pay loggers a "straight-through" price by species. The mill's procurement forester will take a look at the woodlot and negotiate a price with the logger to buy all of the oak or maple sawlogs at a single price per MBF regardless of grade.

Then, in his negotiations with the landowner, the logger will factor in his approximation of the cost of working on that particular lot, and the offered prices for the various products will be based on that understanding. The least expensive logging job is on a lot that has a high volume of large-diameter trees, a good internal road system over flat, dry ground with a central landing and short skidding distance. Higher logging costs result when one or more of the above conditions is less than ideal. The underlying principles are simple: the more difficult it is to operate, the less wood that gets brought to the market, and the higher the per-unit cost. The cost for cutting and yarding normally ranges from $100/MBF to $250/MBF, but in some circumstances it can reach more than $500/MBF.

In this scenario, the logger serves as a middle man, and he is compensated not only for felling, yarding, and trucking but also for marketing the wood. In this schedule, the logger receives as little as $105/MBF for a log priced a penny above the $150/MBF rate, but considerably more

for veneer. If veneer were sold at a rate of $2,400, for instance, the logger would be paid $600/MBF, with $1,800/MBF going to the landowner. There's a straightforward reason for this discrepancy. It's in the landowner's interest to have every log sold at as high a price as possible, and increased payment for the higher grades gives the logger an incentive to bring logs to their best markets.

A logger needs to earn a base rate for his services. His operating costs are the same whether he cuts a firewood tree or a veneer tree. When the products have little value, as can sometimes be the case for certain species of pulp (in the above example, pine), the stumpage payment to the landowner might be nearly nothing, because the logger's expenses and need for profit haven't been met. When the logger makes out well financially, he will not need to cut corners to make ends meet. He can work carefully, the way you want him to. Loggers and foresters speak the same language and understand the nuances of the work and the markets. Having a forester negotiating a price that works for you and for the logger is your best assurance that the harvest will be a success. Payment schedules based on the value of products sold have proven to work well for both loggers and landowners.

You may ask, and rightly so, "Isn't this the same as selling logs, not trees?" In the eyes of the IRS—and theirs are the eyes that count—it's not. If you've ever purchased farm-raised meat from a neighbor, it's a similar situation. Unless specifically licensed to do so, a farmer can't legally sell you cuts of meat, but he can sell you a live animal. He arranges for the slaughter and the cutting of the meat to your specifications—"no shoulder roasts, lots of ground meat, please"—and all parties, including the U.S. Department of Agriculture officials, are satisfied. Same thing with trees: you make an agreement to sell the standing trees at a price that's based on what will be cut from them.

The discussion of pay-as-cut has thus far described a situation in which the forester relies on the logger to market the logs. This is common, and many foresters develop long-term relationships with a handpicked cadre of loggers, and defer to them to do the marketing. Those foresters who market wood for landowners themselves work with loggers who are paid a certain amount per MBF or per cord to cut and yard trees. The price per unit changes according to the working conditions of the job site. Note that in this situation, you are selling logs, not trees. As mentioned above, the additional reporting requirements to the IRS might make this method unattractive.

ENVIRONMENTAL CONSIDERATIONS

At the start of this chapter, I wrote that a good timber sale experience will produce an acceptable financial gain and a change in the conditions of your woods that meets your objectives. The changed conditions are primarily in the forest structure and in the growing environment for the trees that continue on. As we noted, logging is a messy business because, in almost all cases, heavy equipment is involved.

The logger should follow operational standards (known as best management practices) to ensure that the changes to your forest don't also include loss of soil, altered streamflows, damaged roots, and compacted soil. The changes should not compromise the system.

To remove timber, you need to use roads, trails, and a landing (or header, or yard, from which springs the verb "to yard"). If they are not already in place, they will need to be built, and the cost of doing so will reduce the revenue from the first timber sale. (In cases where there's little standing value, these start-up costs can even wipe out the income.) Some properties provide a perfect situation for laying out roads and a landing. Other parcels can have a peculiar boundary shape or be so wet, steep, or rough with bedrock that it takes an engineering visionary to figure out a site for a landing and the roads going to and from it.

A landing needs to be mostly flat, and large enough and dry enough to support the accumulation, sorting, and loading of logs. The minimum size will vary depending on the mix of equipment that's involved in the harvesting; mechanical harvesting equipment and tractor-trailers need room to maneuver. If space for a landing is limited, that can dictate the choice of equipment. The smallest landing you can get away with is a drive-through landing or one that allows the trucker to back into it readily and then drive out fully loaded.

Count on at least a 1-acre opening in your forest that is reached via a road wide enough to accommodate a fully loaded

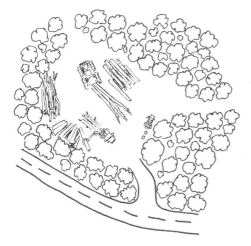

Figure 8.2   A log landing is a busy place, and it needs to be large enough to accommodate skidders delivering logs and log trucks turning around before they load themselves and leave with a load of logs.

log truck. That road is for getting the logs from the landing to the market. Bringing the felled trees (or logs) from where they stood to the landing is accomplished with a network of skid trails. A classic design is shaped like a tree with a main trunk and side branches. This design allows for repeated back and forth traffic on the trunk road, a few passes on each of the branches, and no traffic on the majority of the ground. Good road layout means that the footprint of roads and trails can be minimized.

Skid trails, roads, and landings present the greatest potential for problems on a logging job. Then, there's water. If you have a stream, brook, or river on your land, protecting it is another high priority. Each state has a set of guidelines designed to ensure that logging operations

do not degrade water quality. These are called best management practices or BMPs (in Vermont, they're called acceptable management practices or AMPs), and foresters and loggers should know them chapter and verse. BMPs cover:

- Designing and building landings, truck roads, and skid roads
- Minimizing soil disturbance
- Operating conditions, as in not operating when soils are excessively wet
- Seeding, mulching, and using water control structures (culverts, dips, water bars) to control surface runoff, thereby reducing erosion
- Closing out the job

Except for very short runs, the roads and trails should not be built straight up a hill, but rather across its slope. That's because a road can easily become a streambed that collects rain and snowmelt and carries it downhill. Along with the water goes the soil as the stream gains size and momentum. This can be avoided by minimizing the grade at the design phase, and by installing waterbars when the job is complete.

Waterbars are berms built at an angle across the road, diverting water to the side. They need to be large enough to stop the water's momentum. After the logger has brought the last hitch to the landing, he should go back to the trails and roads to install waterbars. (That won't be possible in winter, because roads and trails freeze to considerable depth, making installation of waterbars nearly impossible. In that case, a shovel is the best tool, and it should be deployed as soon as the ground

Figure 8.3   This waterbar diverts water that might otherwise accumulate and erode the skid trail.

has thawed.) BMPs provide guidelines for the spacing of waterbars depending on the trail's slope. In addition, the steepest sections of road or trail might need to be seeded with an annual grass as a last step. Any unsold wood should be removed from the landing, and in most cases, landings should be seeded.

Conscientious loggers do everything in their power to avoid doing any damage to springs, seeps, streams, wetlands, and any other landscape features that hold water. It is always a challenge because nature can confound the best laid plans.

In many cases, it will be necessary to cross a stream. Depending on the size of the stream, a crossing can be as simple as the winter practice of brushing it in, which means laying small wood across it to drive over, or as complicated as installing a bridge. Most state forestry departments in the Northeast now have programs in which they loan or rent temporary skidder bridges to loggers. These keep heavy equipment out of streams and do a great job protecting water quality. BMPs address stream crossings and, at a minimum, require that the stream crossing be perpendicular to the streambed.

In addition, BMPs set guidelines for how close equipment can go to streams and rivers. Uncut buffer strips along watercourses reduce their sediment load and keep the water cool.

SEASON

In the Northeast, it seems that we are doubly blessed: we have two mud seasons instead of just one in spring, when snow is melting and April showers are trying to bring forth May flowers. The second occurs in September and October, when the leaves stop taking up water from the soil,

slash and bumper trees

*I*n the course of a timber harvest, many landowners wonder what to do with the slash, the unmarketable upper limbs and branches of the cut trees.

A generation ago, standard practice was to leave them untouched, which at least temporarily could make it difficult to walk through a recently harvested forest. Then, it became common to require loggers to cut the larger limbs so the top collapses and doesn't stick up any higher than two or three feet above the ground. Today, we may have reached a happy medium.

If all the slash is kept out of the trails, it's easy to tolerate the mess because of its benefit to the forest system. The tangle of those tops is great cover for amphibians, small mammals, and songbirds, whether it's assembled into piles or left just as it is. The wood rots back into the soil, providing nutrients. There's something else to consider. In areas of high deer density, tree seedlings are constantly being "nipped in the bud." Tree tops that are not lopped can provide a browse barrier for a few years, giving the seedlings a chance to grow.

Still, some landowners find this visually objectionable and ask their foresters: "Why can't the slash be run through a chipper and left in neat

Figure 8.4   The two bumper trees on the bend of this skid trail have lost their bark from having logs skidded against them. They are protecting the tree to the inside of them and will be left in place in anticipation of a future harvest using the same trail.

piles?" The answer is that it can, but it will cost you. That kind of work is very labor intensive and could quickly eat into the revenue you'll receive from selling the stumpage. Furthermore, many loggers will not want to do it. But if that's what you want, you can find someone to accommodate you.

In fact, there are more and more loggers who specialize in that kind of low-visual-impact logging.

Then there are bumper trees, the trees along skid trails, particularly where there is a turn in the trail, that are damaged from logs being skidded against them. Think of them as sacrificial trees that protect other trees from being similarly skinned. Even though they are skinned up, they've served a purpose and should be left in place because in the next harvest they will again keep other trees from being damaged. Though damaged, the bumper trees are unlikely to die from the scraped bark. If you cut them, a tree in better condition will end up playing the role of bumper tree next time there's a harvest. ⊙

---

and soggy conditions in the woods happen all over again. During both of these periods, heavy equipment should not be operating in the woods. There's another reason not to log in spring and early summer. The bark on trees is at its loosest at this stage as water is flowing through the tree's vessels and trees are expanding. Consequently, they are particularly vulnerable to losing bark when a falling tree scrapes against them. These wounds on remaining trees will lead to decay.

Some soils dry up early and allow equipment in: south-facing sunny slopes with sandy soil, and flat outwashes with coarse-graveled soils are the earliest to dry. Other woodlots with a wealth of springs and seeps are wet through much of the year, and the best time to enter them is when it's driest, typically August. Some softwood stands can only be logged in the winter.

EQUIPMENT

The last six decades have seen a remarkable series of changes in the way trees are cut and brought to a landing. Crosscut saws and axes didn't give way to chainsaws until the 1950s, and horses and crawler tractors were still major players well into the 1970s.

Changes have accelerated in the last two decades, and important advances in timber harvest technology common for logging operations on industrial forestland have begun to show up in small, private forests. Today, while the chainsaw in the hands of a logger is still common, more wood is cut by mechanical fellers. A mechanical feller using a machine-mounted saw can closely control the tree's direction of fall and then pile felled trees into a bunch for another machine to transport to a roadside landing. An operator in the

Figure 8.5   a) This cable skidder has just delivered its load to the landing. *b)* Forwarders come in all sizes. This one is pulled by a tractor, and the logger operates the boom with the tractor's hydraulics. *c)* This cut-to-length harvester has removed limbs from a tree and will next cut it into logs of designated lengths. *d)* This grapple skidder grasps its load with its claw-like grapple.

cab of a feller-buncher is far safer than a "chopper" on the ground operating a chainsaw. The most advanced equipment is a "cut-to-length" (CTL) harvester that can fell a tree, remove its limbs, and cut it into prescribed lengths in the woods.

Cut trees or logs are transported to the roadside in one of two ways—skidding or forwarding. Skidders are used to drag a bunch of full-length trees along the ground. They hold the butt ends off the ground to reduce resistance and damage.

A cable skidder can winch each tree to the machine to gather the bunch. Normally, a cable skidder operator will remove those branches too small to be effectively cut into firewood before including the tree in the bunch, which is called a hitch. Cable skidders are most commonly used in conjunction with manual felling. Many loggers continue to operate on their own with a chainsaw and a cable skidder. A grapple skidder is a larger, heavier machine that grabs a pre-bunched hitch with its large, expandable, jaw-like grapple. When whole trees are brought to the landing for chipping, grapple skidders do the work, transporting trunk, limbs, leaves, twigs, and all. These are generally used in concert with a feller-buncher that does the bunching.

Forwarders run on large, balloonish tires or tracks that are designed to better distribute the equipment's weight on the ground. The fully loaded weight is considerable because the forwarder carries logs instead of skidding them—its bunk makes it more like a truck. The forwarder operator uses a boom to load logs onto the bunk—note that they carry logs, not full-length trees. The logs stay clean, and the machine can maneuver in relatively tight spaces. When they arrive at the landing, the boom aids in sorting the logs as they are unloaded.

Which equipment is right for your job? If yours is primarily a biomass harvest, then it will have to be a feller-buncher and a grapple skidder, because they're the only combination effective at getting whole trees to the chipper. This equipment combination processes a lot of wood in a hurry, so a job has to promise enough wood to make it feasible to truck in this heavy artillery. For smaller lots or smaller harvests, the cable skidder and manual felling might be the better choice. Or perhaps, yours is the right job for a cut-to-length processor and forwarder. Another consideration in the matchmaking is that some loggers are better at cutting and marketing hardwoods; others might be better at spruce-fir or pine. Your forester probably works with loggers with a variety of equipment and skills, and should be able to match the crew to the lot.

Each set of equipment has advantages and disadvantages. It's counter-intuitive, but some of the largest equipment can have a small environmental footprint by virtue of low ground pressure and the ability to reach trees without having to drive to each one. A cut-to-length processor and forwarder might seem like the perfect technology for any job because they do so little damage to the ground and to adjacent trees. The one drawback is that forwarders can have difficulty operating on steep slopes because they can be top-heavy and tippy when loaded.

The lines of distinction among the systems can be blurry because loggers tend to be improvisers, always looking for the best combination of equipment for their specific needs. Hand-fellers might use a forwarder instead of a skidder. Some contractors own both a feller-buncher and a CTL harvester.

The crucial factor is the skill and sensitivity of the operator. Any equipment in the hands of a hurried operator can wreak havoc. A horse logger who doesn't know directional felling can damage many adjacent crowns. You'll want to entrust your woods to a logger who has demonstrated proficiency, skill, and strong environmental and business ethics.

How do you know if you've had a good job done? That question has to be answered in two different realms, silvicultural and operational. The silvicultural judgment is necessarily subjective, but here are two questions to answer: Has the harvest accomplished your goals for changes in the conditions in the woods? Will the overall quality of the trees standing at the end of the harvest ultimately be better than it was at the beginning?

In judging the operations, there are more objective measures. Are the roads and trails stable and relatively smooth? Do they have appropriate waterbars, broad-based dips, or culverts in place to move water off to the side? Have the stream crossings been made without any increased sedimentation downstream? Has the work been accomplished with a minimum of damage to standing trees? Are all the cultural features—stonewalls and cellar holes, for instance—intact? Have the boundaries been respected? Is the landing stable and smooth and free of debris? If the answer to all of these is yes, you have indeed had a successful harvest. ◘

CHAPTER 9

FINANCIAL AND TAX IMPLICATIONS

Now that you've had a successful timber sale, you're suddenly awash in cash. Okay, maybe you're not exactly awash, maybe you're up to your ankles in cash. In any event, the Internal Revenue Service is going to want some of that income. And it's not only the feds—you could owe taxes to the state, county, or town as well. Then there's property tax, a carrying cost that enters in regardless of whether you have timber income or not.

Of all the thickets facing the owner of a piece of wooded property, the most impenetrable may be the legal and financial details of paying taxes. I'll try to clear away some of the denser brush and help you understand the tax implications of owning forestland. Take this chapter as general information and not as specific tax advice. For advice about your particular situation, you should consult an accountant.

Here are the taxes that may affect family forest owners:

- Property
- Income
- Capital gains
- Estate
- Severance
- Yield

To illustrate how the tax situation plays out, here's a hypothetical example: let's say that you own a hundred acres of woodland that includes the house where you live. You bought it a few years ago for $350,000. For income tax purposes, you're in the 25 percent IRS income tax bracket, and you live in a state that pegs income taxes at 25 percent of the federal. Your local property taxes are 2.5 percent of the property's value.

Let's take care of the property taxes first. Regardless of which of the three approaches you take—owning woodlands as a hobby, investment, or business—property tax is a given and can be reduced only through participation in a "current use" program, which I'll cover in detail below. No tax is more vexing to the owner of woodland than property tax for the simple reason that it can serve as constant pressure to do something that you may have no interest in doing: subdividing your forest into house lots and selling it off bit by bit.

All states in the Northeast use *ad valorem* taxation. That means that property is taxed according to its value—let's call it fair market value, as that's the term most often used. Fair market value means the price that a willing buyer will reasonably pay a willing seller. Setting a value in that way seems sensible at first, until you realize that what it means is this: the fair market value is what the land would be worth to a developer who wants to plunk as many houses on it as possible and sell them one by one. That scenario — and the valuation based on it—doesn't necessarily match up with your current use of the land or your vision for its future. You may have decided that your land is best suited for wildlife habitat, a network of hiking trails, and an occasional timber harvest, but that doesn't matter to the town assessors. On the open market, your property is worth more than that, and your town has assessed its value at $350,000. At 2.5 percent of its assessed value, your house and land are subject to property taxes of $8,750 each year.

You can reduce the impact of this bill somewhat by deducting it from your state and federal income taxes by filling out Form 1040: Schedule A (Itemized Deductions). In the above example—25 percent federal bracket and with state taxes equal to 25 percent of federal taxes—you would save $2,734 in income taxes, effectively reducing your property tax bill to $6,016.

That helps some, but more relief is available to landowners who are willing to enter into a contract with the state government. Crafters of tax policy in most states in the United States—and every state in the Northeast—acknowledge that taxing land at fair market value can detract from the goal of maintaining a productive rural land base. Consequently, each state has instituted a program that modifies the property tax assessment for landowners who commit to keeping the land in its current undeveloped condition into the future. Generically, these programs are referred to as current use programs. Participating in one can result in a substantial reduction in your property tax bill.

CURRENT USE

The original intent of the property tax, back when it was first applied in colonial days, was to find an equitable way to raise money to fund town government and local education. Real property—land, houses, barns, and livestock—was both easy to see (and therefore assess) and also a reasonable indication of a person's overall wealth and ability to pay taxes. For these reasons, the property tax became the tax of choice for funding local government.

Three and a half centuries later, the idea of taxing property to fund government seems a lot less rational. The amount of real estate a person owns does not necessary relate to his overall wealth. The "land poor" farmer may own 500 acres yet struggle to pay the property tax bill while the savvy stock market investor, living in a duplex on a quarter acre, may have enough money to fund the entire town's operation yet pay relatively little in property taxes.

Recognizing the absurdity of this situation yet lacking a clear mandate to come up with a better system for raising revenues, most states have tweaked their property-based revenue programs through current use programs. The idea is for land to be taxed on its "current use"—for growing trees or crops—rather than at its fair market value as developable land.

The details of current use programs, and their formal names, vary from state to state (see Figure 9.1 on the following page). Generally, however, landowners commit to keeping their land in forestry or agriculture in exchange for the town or state reducing the tax rate to one that's more commensurate with income earned from forestry or agricultural production. In most states, landowners also must file long-term management plans that outline how the land will be used. Some current use agreements run for fixed lengths of time, with the option to renew, while others last in perpetuity. If a landowner decides at a future time to develop the land, he or she will have to pay a penalty, often including back taxes, to withdraw the land from the program.

Current use programs are not for everyone. They are enforceable contracts through which you give up some of your management flexibility in exchange for a reduced tax bill. Many people find that hard to swallow. If you are unsure of your goals for the land over the next five to ten years, the prospect of a hefty penalty if you decide to subdivide or develop your land should give you pause before signing up. On the other hand, if you know for sure that you plan to keep your land in forestry and agriculture for at least the next decade or so, the financial benefits of being enrolled in current use quickly outweigh the spectre of a future fine. Paying a forester for a management plan can be

expensive, but it's probably worth the expense because current use programs can lower the tax bill on your enrolled land (though not on your house and other residential buildings) by 90 percent or more, particularly if you live in an area with escalating land values. Over time, the value of these savings will quickly exceed the expense of a withdrawal fine that might have to be paid 20 or 30 years down the road.

Current use programs typically require you to cut trees as part of your management plan. Vermont, for example, requires economic activity as part of the justification for the current use tax reduction; it's a land productivity program rather than an open space program. New Hampshire, meanwhile, does not require economic activity, believing that keeping the land open is a sufficient public good. New Hampshire's system employs increasing levels of tax relief according to increased public benefit. Keeping land undeveloped is the lowest relief category; managing it for forestry or agriculture increases the relief; and keeping the land open for public recreation offers additional benefit.

If your state has a management requirement, you will need a formal management plan similar to what we discussed in earlier chapters. Each state has different requirements for a plan, and foresters practicing in the state will be familiar with the procedures. You will be required to follow the details of your management plan, which means you may be somewhat limited in your ability to change your management objectives down the road.

State	Program name	Minimum acreage	Tax valuation	Management plan required?	Withdrawal penalty	Application deadline	Web address
CONNECTICUT	Public Act 490	25 (for forestry)	determined by local assessors	no; certified forester must assess the land	determined by local assessors	31 October	www.ct.gov/doag/cwp/ view.asp?a=1366&q=259834
MAINE	Tree Growth	10	set each year by county and wood type	yes	20–30% of difference between fair market value and valuation for tree growth	1 April	www.maine.gov/doc/mfs/ woodswise/growth.html
MASSACHUSETTS	Chapter 61	10	varies yearly based on economic potential	yes	five years back taxes plus penalty	1 July	www.mass.gov/legis/laws/ mgl/gl-61-toc.htm
NEW HAMPSHIRE	Current Use	10	$15/acre–$170/acre, depending upon management	no	10% of fair market value	15 April	www.nh.gov/revenue/ currentuse/currentuse.htm
NEW YORK	480a Forestry Program	50	approximately 20% of fair market value	yes	2.5 times the accumulated tax savings plus interest	1 January	http://www.dec.ny.gov/ lands/5236.html
RHODE ISLAND	The Farm, Forest & Open Space Act	10	set by towns; roughly $120/acre	yes	up to 10% of fair market value	rolling	www.dem.ri.gov/programs/ bnatres/forest/
VERMONT	Use Value Appraisal	25 (for forestry)	set annually by state; 2011 rate is $95 or $127/acre, depending upon road access	yes	10 or 20% of fair market value of withdrawn land, depending on time enrolled	1 September	www.vtfpr.org/resource/ for_forres_useapp.cfm

Figure 9.1   Current use program for each state in the Northeast as of early 2012.

This plan will need to be updated periodically—every 10 years is common—and any changes in your land use status (converting forest to field or vice versa) may need to be approved beforehand. Digging a pond for swimming and fishing may require removing the affected land from the program, so it's better to plan ahead and exclude that land at the time of enrolling.

When you enroll in a current use program, the appraisal of your property is considered in two parts: the value of your house and the land it sits on (the homestead, as its known in Vermont), and the value of the enrolled land. Of your 100 acres and $350,000 property, for example, the house and homestead might be assessed at $230,000. This portion of the tax bill will not be affected by your enrollment in a current use program. The remaining woodland is assessed at $120,000 (roughly $1,200 per acre), the full market value of the undeveloped land. The current use administrators, meanwhile, will have established a lower figure for undeveloped woodland enrolled in the program. To make the example easy, let's say that the current use rate is set at $120 per acre, meaning that the 100 acres that was valued at $120,000 is now valued at $12,000.

The tax you were paying on the 100 acres, valued at $120,000, was $3,000 per year (at the 2.5 percent rate). Under current use, the same 100 acres, now valued at $12,000, carries a tax bill of $300, saving you $2,700 per year in property taxes. Your property tax bill will have dropped from $8,750 to $6,050. If you now deduct this reduced cost on Schedule A, you will have an effective property tax bill of $4,159.

TIMBER SALE INCOME

Property taxes will seem straightforward in comparison to reporting income from timber sales.

Let's continue with the example of the 100-acre family forest, and we'll assume for the moment that you have followed the advice set forth earlier: you've searched around for a forester and hired the one who seemed to most closely share your own values. After having a good discussion with her about the various options, you have come to a clear understanding of how you want to proceed with managing your land. Based on that, she prepared a management plan for your 100 acres, and with the plan in hand you enrolled your land in the state's current use program. The approved management plan calls for you to conduct an initial improvement cut on 80 acres of your hardwoods and mixedwoods. The other 20 acres is still in a pre-commercial phase, and you resolve to do some timber stand improvement work in there on your own in an attempt to accelerate the growth of the good trees.

Your forester introduced you to the work of a logger she's worked with for years. He has worked in many woodlots quite like yours, and when you visited one of his harvests from three years ago, it made you comfortable that he's the kind of person you could trust. So you entered into a timber sale contract like the one in the appendix.

Your forester marked the trees to be cut and flagged the layout for the roads. As part of the contract, the logger brought

---

severance tax

*T*he term severance tax *could hardly be more fitting in its forestry usage, since it taxes what has been severed.*

In New York, landowners who enroll their forestland in the state's 480a Forestry Program pay a severance tax when they cut timber. They pay 6 percent of the stumpage value to the county.

Several states levy a yield tax of some sort—it may be called a timber tax or something similar—on income derived from selling wood. This tax is typically a small percentage of the gross receipts and must be paid within a certain time frame of the wood being harvested.

In New Hampshire, all timber sales over a certain volume trigger a requirement to notify the town about the harvest. On completion of the harvest, the landowner pays a 10 percent yield tax on the volume cut. The landowner is not required to disclose what he or she actually was paid for the timber. Values for wood are set by the N.H. Department of Revenue Administration, and the town sends the bill for the yield tax to the landowner. ⊙

---

his bulldozer and used it to cut in skid trails and touch up the old woods road that was used by a previous owner to provide access to a small landing. The landing needed to be expanded somewhat, but you were fortunate that you had some infrastructure in place. He charged $70 an hour for 16 hours of bulldozer work.

With the roads in place, the logger worked in your woods for a month or so and harvested lots of firewood and a comparatively small number of sawlogs. He cut a ratio of firewood to sawlogs that is typical of the first improvement cut: from 80 acres, you removed 240 cords of firewood and 40,000 board feet (40 MBF) of sawlogs. Some of the sawlogs brought more than $400/MBF, but the majority of them were in the $100/MBF category, and the stumpage payments averaged $200/MBF.

The following chart shows the income and expenses associated with the job:

Income		
240 cords @ $6/cord		$1,440
40 MBF @ $200/MBF		$8,000
	Total income	$9,440
Expenses		
Management plan		$750
Harvest layout, marking trees, supervision, 40 hours @ $45/hour		$1,800
Road-building, 16 hours @ $70/hour		$1,120
	Total expenses	$3,670
	Net income	$5,770

So your proceeds have not immediately catapulted you into a higher tax bracket, but netting $5,770 is a nice windfall. This income needs to be reported to the IRS and to state taxing authorities, just like

recovering expenses

*I*t's impossible to make a single recommendation to fit all timberland investors' personal situations.

The choice of how you categorize your expenses is one of the forks in the road where a personal guide would be handy, and an accountant familiar with timber investments can help you think through the options.

The options come about because the IRS recognizes that income from a timberland investment is sporadic and that development costs are ongoing. Investors can choose to deduct management expenses in the year they occur. Or you can elect to treat management costs as a carrying charge and therefore add them to the basis of the property.

If you choose the latter, you need to declare this by filing a statement with your return. In this way, any expenses that contribute to an increased value of the asset can be capitalized. If you buy a chainsaw to use for timber stand improvement, you can capitalize it and the fuel to run it.

Doing so might make sense because expenses in the "certain miscellaneous deductions" section of Schedule A need to exceed 2 percent of your adjusted gross income. In some years, your combined timber and non-timber miscellaneous itemized deductions may not be sufficient to put you above the 2 percent floor.

In that case, you will not be able to deduct your timber expenses, and you'll lose them. If you elect to capitalize them as a carrying charge, these expenses are added to the basis of your assets for eventual recovery.

Once you make this election, it applies to all future expenses, so you lose the ability to deduct them each year. Because you can only recover them in a year with timber income, you may be tying up sizable expenses for longer than you wish. Consult an accountant before making the commitment. ⊙

any other income. Income taxes tend to be far less onerous than property taxes, if for no other reason than they only need to be paid when you earn income, which—in terms of income from forestland—most likely will not be every year. How much of your timber sale income goes to the IRS and the state depends on how you sell your timber and which of the three approaches you take to owning your family forest: hobby, investment, or business.

WOODLANDS FOR PERSONAL USE OR HOBBY

The first approach to owning woodland is to view your land as something held entirely for personal use or as a hobby. This doesn't mean you're completely off the hook if you have a timber sale. You still need to report the income on Form 1099-S and pay income tax on it.

The other form that comes into play is Schedule D, where you report capital gains income. That's right, income from selling timber is a capital gain, rather than ordinary income, as long as you have held the asset for at least one year. If you've owned the land less than a year, sale income is a short-term capital gain, which is taxed at the ordinary income rate.

The way you handle your timber-related expenses is the main difference between treating your forestland as a hobby or as an investment, which is the second and more advantageous approach. A hobby owner can deduct expenses only to offset income. In years with no sales, you can't deduct any expenses, and they could be considerable. If your forester completes your management plan this year, but you won't have any income until a sale scheduled three years from now, you can't deduct that expense until then, if you're a hobby landowner. It's not that you lose the expense deduction; you can capitalize it, which means you add it to the cost basis of the land. If you're an investor, however, you can deduct those expenses in the year they occur.

WOODLAND AS AN INVESTMENT

What makes you an investor? To be considered an investor, all you need to do is show an intent to make a profit from the investment. Some signals of intent: hire a forester to manage your forest; in your management plan, state your intention to increase the value of your forest; make prudent use of your investment dollars. Owning timberland is an investment that generates sporadic income—your timber sales will be only occasional—and has the potential for substantial growth through capital appreciation.

Let's look at the details of your timber sale again. After expenses, you cleared $5,770. If you report it as income from capital gains, taxes are 15 percent, assuming you've owned the asset (in this case, your woodlands) for at least 12 months. Add in a quarter of that for the state, and you're up to 18.75 percent, for a total tax bill of $1,082. But that's only the first step, because the 18.75 percent is not applied to the profit; instead, it is applied to the profit less what you paid for the asset. The formula for determining your capital gain is income minus expenses minus cost basis equals capital gain.

The realist in you might say, "That's a good situation. What's the downside?" And there is one, because the amount of recordkeeping and engagement with the tax code increases considerably when you treat your woodlands as an investment. To satisfy the IRS, you'll be keeping detailed records of what expenses you incur and when you incur them, and you'll be delving into devilish accounting principles such as depletion allowances and adjusted cost basis. You also may be hiring a professional tax preparer to guide you through the thicket. The savings are not small potatoes, though, and most forestland owners should consider it well worth their time to do the paperwork.

CAPITAL GAINS — ESTABLISHING BASIS

For tax purposes, the IRS allows trees to be considered capital assets, much like the parcel of land that they are growing on. (The exception to this is if the owner of the trees is in the primary business of selling wood products—firewood, for example, or milled lumber.) Capital assets change in value over time, and the tax on that new value is due only when this value change is realized, that is, when the assets are sold. Here's where the significant recordkeeping comes into play.

To figure out how much an asset has changed in value when it comes time to sell it, you first have to know how much you paid for it. This initial value is known as the tax basis of the asset. In the example we're using for this chapter, you paid $350,000 two years ago for your house and woodland. This purchase price establishes the tax basis for the entire property—$350,000.

You need to be able to document this tax basis should the IRS ever decide to audit your return, so be sure to keep a copy of your closing statement, preferably in a safe-deposit box. If you can't lay your hands on a copy of the closing statement during the audit and can't establish a fair basis for the asset, the IRS would be within its rights to set the tax basis of the property equal to $0. "Who knows?" the agent could say with a smirk. "Maybe the property was given to you." In other words, recordkeeping is key: no records, no basis; no basis, no way to avoid paying taxes on the asset's full market value.

That's not so difficult, you say. But it's about to get much trickier, because it's not your house and land that you are selling in a timber sale, it's the trees. What is your cost basis in the trees?

Since you bought the property recently, it will be easy to establish the relative value of the house and lot, underlying land, and timber. And that's what you need to do: separate it into accounts. Your town assessor can help you establish the separate values of the house and lot (we'll call it the homestead) and the underlying land. Your forester, since she has done a timber cruise, can help you ascertain the value of the timber.

The assessor has access to data on sales of comparable houses with an acre or two attached and tells you the homestead is worth $230,000. Bare land in the area, yes, bare—void of trees and not growing lush pasture grass because it's a sea of stumps—is worth $1,000 an acre, so that's $100,000. Your forester's cruise shows that your forestland contains 300 MBF of sawlogs and 2,000 cords of pulp for a timber value of $70,000.

The total of the three separate accounts is $400,000. That makes you happy because it confirms that you struck a good deal in buying the property for $350,000. That doesn't mean that your basis is $400,000—your basis is what you paid for it (plus improvements, which we'll discuss below), not what it might have been worth. So you need to do another calculation, which is to figure out the relative value of the three accounts and apply it to the purchase price. Through this exercise, you determine that the timber basis is

Timber accounts separated into sub-accounts

Sub-account	Unit	Volume	$/unit	FMV	Basis	Adjusted basis
Sawtimber	MBF	300	$200	$60,000	$52,491	$54,094
Pulpwood	cord	2,000	$5	$10,000	$8,759	$9,026
				$70,000	$61,250	$63,120
				Addition to basis	$1,870	
				Adjusted basis	$63,120	

$61,250. The accounts need to get subdivided into separate accounts for sawlogs and pulpwood to help you make the next calculation, the depletion allowance.

Cost basis separated into accounts

Account	Fair market value	% of FMV	Cost basis
Homestead	$230,000	57.5	$201,250
Bare land	$100,000	25.0	$87,500
Timber	$70,000	17.5	$61,250
Total	$400,000		$350,000

That initial basis is increased by any investments you make that add to the timberland's value. In our example, woods roads are a long-term capital improvement to the land that increases the value of the asset, so you add that expense to your basis. And you would add the forester's charge for developing the management plan, which includes cruising the timber. On the other hand, her fee for administering the timber sale is an expense specific to this sale, so it will be an expense, not an addition to the basis.

You can also capitalize (meaning add to your cost basis) carrying costs—property taxes, insurance, and mortgage interest—assuming you aren't already item-izing them on Schedule A (see summary table above).

Your adjusted basis, after adding the roadwork and management plan expenses to the basis, is $63,120. Your basis in the 300 MBF of sawlogs is $54,094; your basis in the 2,000 cords of pulpwood is $9,026.

DEPLETING YOUR BASIS

For natural resources that are harvested or extracted over time, like timber or minerals or oil, the IRS allows the tax basis to be "depleted" over time as the original asset is used up. In other words, if you cut half of your timber, you can deduct half of your basis from the sale and save the other half for later.

Timber is different from the other natural resources in two ways: first, you can measure it much more readily than you can the natural gas or oil under your ground. And second, trees grow. In a year's time, today's volume will be increased by 2 percent or more. In selling timber, you rarely sell all of it at once. Instead, you harvest a percentage of it every now and again. And the overall volume keeps increasing between harvests. This means that you'll be referring to the tax basis more than

Computing depletion units

Account	Basis	Original volume	Depletion unit	Harvest volume	Depletion allowance	Remaining basis
Sawtimber	$54,094	300	$180.31	40	$7,212	$46,882
Pulpwood	$9,026	2,000	$4.51	240	$1,082	$7,944
					$8,294	$54,826

once and changing it every time you do so. This brings us to the depletion allowance.

Your adjusted basis, with the addition of the expenses, is $63,120, split into the two accounts as shown above. Divide the adjusted basis by the original volume and you'll have your depletion units. In this case, you have depletion units of $180.31 per MBF and $4.51 per cord. You depleted 40 MBF for a depletion allowance of $7,212; you depleted 240 cords for a depletion allowance of $1,082.

These depletion allowances are used in calculating your long-term capital gain. (It's long-term because you owned the asset for longer than one year.) Here's the calculation:

Gross income, less sale expenses, less depletion allowance = Capital gain	
Gross income	$9,440
Sale expenses	$1,800
Depletion allowance	$8,294
Capital gain	($654)

By using $8,294 of your basis, you have reduced your adjusted cost basis to $54,826. When the next harvest comes around, you will need to re-establish your depletion units by dividing the remaining basis by the new volume of timber growing at that time. If, for example, the next harvest is 10 years later, and the volume of timber has

increased from 260 MBF to 317 MBF and pulpwood from 1,760 cords to 2,145, the new depletion allowance would be $147.92 per MBF and $3.70 per cord.

More importantly, the rather stunning result is that you now have a capital loss of $654 that you can use to offset any capital gains from sales of stocks or other assets held longer than one year. You have reduced your tax on the timber sale to zero by going through all the requisite record-keeping and calculations. In this scenario, your basis and the receipts from the timber sale are very close because it all took place within two years.

LONG-TERM OWNERSHIP

Some readers are getting antsy at this point, especially those who bought their land years ago. Let's just change one detail in our scenario—the length of ownership—and see how that plays out. Instead of purchasing two years ago, you purchased 20 years ago, and it wasn't until just now that you have gotten interested in forestry and had your first timber cruise.

This does indeed make the paperwork more complicated, but it's by no means impossible. Step one is to work from the timber cruise, which establishes today's volume and value. Then have your forester

Cost basis for purchase made 20 years ago

Account	Fair market value	% of FMV	Cost basis
Homestead	$230,000	64.56	$225,960
Bare land	$100,000	28.07	$98,243
Timber	$26,258	7.37	$25,797
	$356,258		$350,000

Timber accounts separated into sub-accounts

Sub-account	Unit	Volume	$/unit	FMV	Basis	Adjusted basis
Sawtimber	MBF	202	$110	$22,220	$21,830	$23,412
Pulpwood	cords	1,346	$3	$4,038	$3,967	$4,255
				$26,258	$25,797	$27,667
			Addition to basis		$1,870	
			Adjusted basis		$27,667	

Computing depletion units

Account	Basis	Original volume	Depletion unit	Harvest volume	Depletion allowance	Remaining basis
Sawtimber	$23,412	202	$115.90	40	$4,636	$18,776
Pulpwood	$4,255	1,346	$3.16	240	$759	$3,496
					$5,395	$22,272

work backward in time to determine what volumes of sawlogs and cordwood came with your purchase. Because she knows your land and its site conditions, she can make a good estimate of an annual growth rate. With that in hand, she discounts at that growth rate—let's say it's 2 percent—and calculates the volume 20 years ago. In other words, the volume of wood was 2 percent per year less going back 20 years. The volumes from 20 years ago work out to be 202 MBF and 1,346 cords.

Your forester examines stumpage receipts from 20 years ago and determines that the stumpage value of your species mix of sawtimber at that time was $110 as opposed to the current $200. The price of cordwood essentially tracked inflation, so it was worth $3 per cord. At the same time, you need to document the value of the homestead and the bare land 20 years ago. Again, your town assessor or a realtor should be able to help you with this. You learn that, with the various rises and falls, the value of your homestead and bare land have held steady, so you use the same figures. With the lower timber values, your overall basis is closer to your purchase price of $350,000. It's $356,246. Cost basis for the 202 MBF of sawtimber is $21,830; basis for the 1,346 cords is $3,967 (above).

We'll substitute those numbers and redo the calculation. Your income and expense are the same. (We haven't accounted for the cost of having your forester do the regression in volume. This is not a trivial exercise, so there will be a few hours of additional expenses.)

Gross income, less sale expenses, less depletion allowance = Capital gain	
Gross income	$9,440
Sale expenses	$1,800
Depletion allowance	$5,395
Capital gain	$2,245

What's different is your cost basis. Selling timber today that you bought 20 years ago makes a difference. Because the volume is relatively low—this is, after all, only an initial improvement cut—the difference isn't startling. Your gain is $2,245 instead of a loss of $654. Now, you will owe capital gains tax of $421. If you couldn't establish a basis, the gain would have been $5,770. Instead of adding road building and management plan expenses to the basis, you would expense them, so your income of $9,440 would be offset by expenses of $3,670 and your capital gains tax would have been $1,082.

As you can see, you can save substantial sums of money by treating sales of your trees as a capital gain instead of as ordinary income, and you can save even more by establishing the tax basis of those trees instead of paying tax on the full sale price.

In a third scenario, if you bought your land 40 years ago, and the woodland was just starting off as second-growth saplings that didn't have much value, it won't be worthwhile to pay the forester to adjust your basis. Just set the basis equal to zero. The general rule is that the longer ago and the younger the wood when you bought the land, the less effort should be expended to determine the original basis. If you bought a stand of high-quality, 12-inch-diameter oak 10 years ago, by all means pay the forester to do the work. If you bought pasture pine and poplar saplings 30 years ago, skip it.

T IS FOR TIMBER

As I mentioned earlier, good recordkeeping is an essential aspect of active woodland management. You will need to have a system in place that allows you to easily keep track of your capital improvements, adjusted basis, and depreciation allowance, and this system needs to be clear enough that you can return to it after long periods of no timber harvesting and remember what it means. Even more important, the IRS needs to be able to decipher what it means in the event of an audit. To follow the IRS approach, use Form T (Timber): Forest Activities Schedule for tracking your woodlands-as-capital-investment tax filings. This form provides a framework that ensures that you have not forgotten (or misallocated) income and expenses.

You can download Form T and its instructions from the IRS website. Examining how it looks at timber investments will help you understand the kinds of records that you should keep, and how they are reported. If your timber sales are infrequent—in IRS language, "one or two every three or four years"—you don't need to file Form T. Instead you can file a statement that shows how you came to your calculations. This should suffice.

PROFITABLE ENTERPRISE?

This discussion of income and expense —along with the share that goes to the taxman—may prompt you to ask: can you make a profit from owning and managing a family forest?

We know that money can be made from large holdings. Timberland investment management organizations (TIMOs) and some large family holdings have proven that forestland makes sense as an investment, but their acreage is measured more readily in square miles than acres. At that scale, fixed costs get spread across many acres, and harvest income comes annually by rotating through the various stands. In the case of the TIMOs, the equation most often includes buying at an attractive price, earning some income along the way from different revenue streams—timber sales, camp leases, recreational fees, conservation easements—and then selling into a market hungry for timberland. A forest is not a particularly liquid asset, however, so it will be a challenge for some of the current investors to find the right moment to implement their exit strategy.

Family ownerships, even those of 10,000 or more acres, are more likely to be longer term investments because people get attached to land. There's an emotional connection that doesn't exist with a stock portfolio. When land holdings are 1,000 acres or less, it's more difficult for an owner to regularly make a profit from timber sales alone. Let me present a best case scenario of a very productive forest. It's 1,000 acres of very productive soils growing northern hardwoods. It holds 30 cords to the acre, and the timber is growing at a rate of 5 percent a year, better than the region-wide average of 3 percent.

If all the trees were of sawtimber quality, it would hold 15 MBF per acre, using a conversion of 2 cords per MBF. If that sawtimber had an average stumpage value of $250, you'd own $3.75 million worth of timber on your 1,000 acres. It's hard to picture a scenario this good, and this might only be possible on paper and not in the woods. On the other hand, the 1,000 acres won't hold only cordwood; if it did, at $5 a cord, your 1,000 acres holds $150,000 of stumpage value. A reasonable guess is a value somewhere in between; on fine soils, with a history of good management, the proportion of sawtimber might be as much as 60 percent.

Timber value on 1,000 acres

Unit	Quantity	Per unit value	Value
Cords	12,000	$5	$60,000
MBF	9,000	$250	$2,250,000
			$2,310,000

If you were to manage aggressively, while making sure that you harvested less than the annual growth, your harvests might over time average 3 percent of the annual growth. The forest would still have net growth of 2 percent per year.

Annual harvest at 3 percent

Unit	Quantity	Per unit value	Value
Cords	360	$5	$1,800
MBF	270	$250	$67,500
			$69,300

Before any expenses, you'd be grossing $69,300 a year. Reduce that by the cost of a forester, property taxes, annual maintenance, roads, and timber stand improvements, and you might still have $50,000 to show for it. That's $50 an acre per year. How do you increase that income? Assuming you're not interested in liquidating the property, but in working with it to make it even more valuable, there are two general opportunities.

First, you could add value to your wood products by not selling just truckloads of sawlogs and firewood. Instead, you could further process either or both. You could buy a firewood processor and turn your 360 cords of log-length wood into 360 cords of cut and split wood. Since it's hard to sell firewood without delivering it, you could buy a dump truck to deliver it. Instead of $5 a cord, now you're grossing $160 a cord. On the lumber side, you might want to buy a portable sawmill and process some of your logs into lumber.

Second, you could diversify your revenue streams. Forestland can produce income in a number of different ways. You could, for instance:

- Devote a portion of it to growing Christmas trees
- Lease 50 suitable acres to a sugarmaker
- Lease the entire property to a group of hunters
- Lease hilltops for cell towers or wind turbines

These sources of revenue are usually all ordinary income (not capital gains), taxed at the taxpayer's individual marginal income tax rate. Each of them has its own pluses and minuses, but you get the picture. To make money from for-

estland, you really need to treat it like a business—which brings us to the third approach, owning woodlands as a business. If you are interested in spending a considerable amount of time managing your land for income, it will most likely become a business, rather than an investment. And don't think for a moment that you can't have a successful small business if your acreage is closer to 50 than 1,000. Your timber harvests will be infrequent, but if you're creative, you can come up with other means of earning regular income that exceeds your expenses.

WOODLAND AS A BUSINESS PROPOSITION

It may not be up to you. The IRS may decide that your woodland ownership is a business, regardless of how you want them to view it.

This brings us back to the point made in Chapter 8 about the importance of stumpage timber sales. If your intention is to make sure that your woodland ownership is viewed as a capital investment by the IRS, be sure to sell your timber as stumpage and not in any other way that could be interpreted as a value-added wood product. Remember the earlier analogy: sell the lamb or steer on the hoof, not as loin chops or prime rib. From the IRS's perspective, income derived from trees sold when attached to the stump is a capital gain, while income derived from trees already lying on the ground is ordinary income.

If you are in the business of selling almost any woods-related product besides stumpage, the IRS is likely to view your trees as a business expense and not as a capital asset. This is true even if you are selling rough-cut lumber milled from your own trees or firewood cut from your own woodlot. The theory is that your trees are acting as raw material for your business—as a business expense or "cost of goods sold" —not as a capital asset. As such, the income from products made from them are subject to income tax, not capital gains tax. You can treat some of it as a capital gain rather than ordinary income by electing to be treated under Section 631(a). The timber must be used in your business, and not for personal use. Electing 631(a) puts it in effect for the current year and all that follow. It can only be discontinued with the permission of the IRS.

If you have gotten gung-ho about the business potential of your land, there are doubtless all sorts of ongoing expenses. Depending on their nature, these expenses might be lost to you if your land is an investment, but they can be recouped for tax purposes if you're treating your land management as a business. This is the key advantage of treating your woodland ownership as a business: short-term losses can be deducted against other income, be it yours from other jobs or investments or your spouse's.

WHAT MAKES A BUSINESS?

The IRS has two tests for determining who is in business and who isn't. Number one is that the business must either show a profit or else act like a business that's intending to show a profit. Number two is that the business owner must materially participate in the running of the business. The idea is to weed out people who invest in money-losing tax shelters solely as a way of reducing the tax they owe.

The simplest test of the profit motive is that the business's tax returns show a profit in three years out of the past five. In the business of land management, however, this is often an unobtainable goal for the simple reason that wood might not be cut for years on end, followed by a single large sale. The business's tax return may show many years of small losses (annual expenses like marking boundary blazes, grading roads, or buying chainsaw gas without any income earned from a timber sale) followed by a single year of substantial profit when the timber is cut. This will not satisfy the IRS. Instead, the woodland owner is obligated to meet several other criteria.

The first is that the business must demonstrate the intention to earn a profit and must act like a business. This means that the activity of the business has to be separated from that of its owner. One way to accomplish that is to establish the business as a limited liability company (LLC) or corporation. Having a business checking account, keeping vendor and customer receipts, belonging to relevant business associations, and being recognized by others as being in business shows that the business is operating apart from its owners.

The second criterion is that the business owner must demonstrate active involvement in the business. Active involvement can be determined in a number of ways, but the simplest is that the owner puts in at least 100 hours of labor per year into the business, and no one else puts in more. If an employee provides more substantial services than the 100 hours, then the threshold becomes higher. As with everything else related to the IRS, it is crucial that you keep good records that document this labor. You might include time sheets, business diaries, or copies of a personal calendar showing dates and hours devoted to working in the business.

Since losses from a business can be deducted against income earned elsewhere (such as wages or salaries), there is a motivation for people to set up bogus businesses that shield their income from taxation. The IRS wants to sort out those people who are losing money in the short term but are nevertheless genuinely trying to earn a profit from those who are merely trying to hide their income. The litmus test is whether or not the person is actively involved in the business. Greater than 100 documented hours per year, and the person is actively involved. Fewer than 100 hours, and the person's involvement is defined as passive.

This makes a big difference when it comes to taxes paid. The passive investor can only deduct business losses against income earned from other passive business interests. In other words, if a person is passively involved in two woodland businesses, one of which earns a profit of $10,000 one year and another that loses $20,000 the same year, the person can use half of the $20,000 loss to reduce the $10,000 gain to zero but cannot take the remaining $10,000 to deduct against income earned, say, at a $40,000-per-year salaried job. Pas-

sive losses can only be deducted from passive income, though unused passive losses can be carried forward.

Active losses, meanwhile, can be deducted from any type of income, be it from other active gains, passive gains, wages and salaries, or other capital gains. This makes it a very useful tool, and one that the IRS is eager to limit only to those who should genuinely be able to use it. If you lose $10,000 in your woodland business one year, you can use that to reduce your income tax bill on the $40,000 you earned that same year at your salaried job.

SETTING UP YOUR BUSINESS

One hundred hours is not a trivial amount of time, nor is the associated recordkeeping and business-like activity that it entails. If you genuinely plan to spend lots of time in your woods, thinning and tinkering and fixing road drainage, and also plan to join woodland associations and hire foresters, loggers, and surveyors on a somewhat regular basis, and want to sell firewood or lumber to your friends and neighbors, then set up a business.

If you're not sure you can make that commitment into the future, you're probably better off staying with the "woodlands as investment" approach. If, in the end, the IRS decides that you're a passive business owner after all and not eligible to deduct your woodland expenses against other income, you would have been much better off taking the capital gains route to begin with. Otherwise, you'll have to pay any back taxes you would have owed plus interest and penalties.

Assuming you're still on board, you will establish your business most likely as a single member LLC or as a sole proprietor, meaning that you will pay taxes on your business income through the regular IRS Form 1040. (The alternatives, setting up your business as a C-corporation or S-corporation, are much more involved, more expensive, and more suited to businesses with multiple investors, multiple employees, and much more "business-like" behavior than your typical woodland ownership.) Schedule C is the form that most woodland business owners use to report their income and expenses, though Schedule F, the business form designed for farming, can also be used. Whichever route you or your tax preparer decide to go, just make sure to stick with the same form from year to year.

Your state may also have annual incorporation fees or business tax forms that need to be filed. Once again, check with experts in your state to make sure that your bases are covered.

Finally, work with a professional tax preparer before deciding how your business will handle its capital assets—the trees themselves. Trees shift from being capital assets to ordinary assets the moment they are severed from the stump; if your business already has sold the trees to an outside buyer at that point, the tax liability will be different than if you've felled them yourself with the intention of turning them into firewood or lumber for later sale. Section 631 of the Internal Revenue Code discusses the details of these two cases and how to keep track of them on Form T (Timber), which is important since a portion of the sale could qualify for capital gain treatment under this section.

The three different approaches to owning your family forest—woodlands as a hobby, investment, or business—are more or less available to everyone who owns woodland. There are financial and time constraints associated with each one, of course, but the ultimate decision on how you decide to view your own woodlands will be a personal decision. Ultimately, you want your woodlands to enhance your life and bring you years of joy. If delving into the tax code and the various possibilities of ownership help bring you that joy, so much the better. If not, you're under no obligation to choose any particular approach besides the one that makes you the happiest and ensures good stewardship of the forest, now and into the future. ☐

CHAPTER 10

THE FUTURE OF YOUR FOREST

What will happen to your land after you're gone?

We've dealt with taxes, so it's perhaps predictable that our next and last stop will be the other inevitability, death. If you've spent a chunk of your life trying to do the right thing with your forestland, you probably have strong feelings about how you want your land to be treated after your tenure is over. No, you can't take it with you, but, whether you bequeath it to your heirs or sell or give it away while still living, you can influence the future of your family forest in a positive way by planning now.

Land has a powerful pull on people. It means much more to most of us than other investments. You don't hear people speaking wistfully about the future of their 3,000 shares of Coca-Cola.

Personally, the last thing I want to have happen to my beloved forest is for it to be carved up into bite-sized pieces. I want it to continue to be a viable forest, full of wildlife and producing high-quality timber to benefit future owners. I expect that some, if not most, readers will share that perspective. The part of the Northeast that is truly rural is shrinking, as the spreading impulse to "get away from it all" incre-

mentally turns the forested landscape into something more suburban. This parcelization of our forests has two important and negative impacts: the loss of habitat and the loss of forestry infrastructure.

Redrawing ownership lines does not automatically reduce habitat, but once the owner of that new parcel clears land for a house and puts in a road, the habitat becomes fragmented. The effects are significant, both for the larger, secretive species like bear and bobcat, and for the diminutive amphibians and reptiles, for whom even a driveway can create an impassable barrier. Fragmentation can also open the door to invasive exotic plants that find convenient entrance to the woods along roads and driveways. One subdivision seems inexorably to lead to the next, so the relentless parcelization of large tracts of forestland into small lots has ill effects on the habitat of many species.

The second loss from parcelization is to the infrastructure that makes good forestry possible. Without a forestland base of parcels large enough for loggers and foresters to work on, the overall capacity of the forest-based economy is diminished. With fewer viable blocks of forestland, fewer loggers and foresters can work in the area. At some point, the diminished output causes a sawmill to be shuttered, then a trucker finds another line of work, then a furniture business lays off its workers. Forestry is a web made up of many strands, and at this point in the twenty-first century, this web cannot stand to become much more sparse. Making the comparison to agriculture is instructive: feed stores, farmhands, tractor dealers, and tillable land are interrelated elements that all need to be present for agriculture to survive. In many parts of the Northeast, that agricultural infrastructure is gone. Forestry continues to survive in much of the region, and the center of the forestry web is the land base of large parcels.

For a logging contractor to move equipment to a woodlot and set up a landing, the job has to have a large enough volume to make it economically worthwhile. Too

few acres can mean not enough marketable wood, so there is no incentive for the logger to go to the trouble unless the owner is willing to forgo income, or—amazing to think—even pay to have work done. At a certain point, there's no longer a financial incentive to manage the forest.

The parcelization of the landscape is a remarkable and relentless phenomenon. The average size of a forest ownership in Vermont is now 44 acres; in New Hampshire, 28.5; and in New York, 21. In Massachusetts, the average size ownership of forestland is now just 7.4 acres. There are as many reasons for this as there are sellers of land: dramatic increases in land value may increase the temptation to cash in, even a little at a time; maybe a child is going to college, and a parcel needs to be sold to help pay for tuition; perhaps that child's older brother wants to build a house and can't afford to buy a building

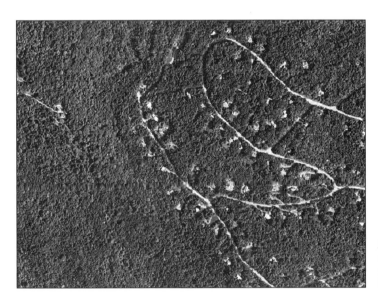

Figure 10.1 Building roads and houses in the interior of forests fragments wildlife habitat.

Figure 10.2   Land-use professionals can help you decide the future of your forest. *Photo courtesy of The Trustees of Reservations.*

lot, so another piece is separated. As we have all seen, financial reversals can happen—catastrophic illness, business failures, uninsured losses—and the one valuable and probably most expendable asset, the land, can help stave off financial disaster by being subdivided or sold outright.

Some of these situations are unavoidable, but it is particularly lamentable when the breakup of an intact forest happens through a simple lack of foresight or understanding. For instance, when a couple with more than one child decides that the fair and equitable thing is to make provisions in the will giving each of the children a part of the land, it is often a recipe for dissolution. I'm reminded of a scene in *One Flew Over the Cuckoo's Nest*, in which McMurphy (Jack Nicholson) has organized a poker game, and the stakes are cigarettes. A cigarette is worth a dime. A timid inmate named Martini wants to bet only a nickel, so he breaks his cigarette in two. McMurphy repeatedly has to explain to Martini that if you break it in

half, you don't get two nickels. "Try and smoke it," he says. "You understand?"

Bequeathing to children half—or a third, or a quarter—of what for many years was the wonderful core of family life might cause it to lose all its value, except its liquidation value. It can become just an asset to be converted to cash. Problems also can arise if undivided interests in the property are willed to two or more siblings with different life situations, different attachments to the place, different needs. If none of them can buy the others out, then a realtor's sign probably will go up on all or part of it.

Having a son or daughter put a second house and driveway on the land may not seem like much of an intrusion. In a vacuum, one more road and one more driveway is not a big deal. When aggregated over the whole Northeast, however, and at the speed with which development has been occurring over the past couple of decades, it compromises the integrity of the ecosystem.

Clearly, the stakes are high. In the first chapter, we cited a study that estimates that more than 60 percent of today's forest owners are older than 55, with more than half of those older than 65. A huge amount of forestland is going to change hands in the next 30 years. Whether that property is transferred after the reading of the will or while the owner is still living and making clear choices can mean the difference between a split up and an intact property.

The good news is that the strong ethic you've brought to managing your land can continue far into the future, if you take steps now to keep your land intact.

TAKING CARE OF HEIRS

The main reason that enlightened forest-land owners end up subdividing their land, despite understanding the pitfalls of parcelization, is they are attempting to treat multiple heirs equitably. If the largest chunk of your potential estate is the land you've loved and tended for years, and on which your children may have grown up and formed lifelong attachments, the impulse to divide the land among them may be overwhelming. What could be more fair?

Historically, dividing the land among heirs was not a feasible economic option when people who owned land were earning the entirety of their income directly from it. Back then, the rule was primogeniture, a tradition in which the eldest received all the land because a certain minimum acreage was necessary for a family to subsist. If it were broken up, there was a danger that the land holding would become too small to support anyone. Now that most people's income is not earned from the land, it is possible to break up land without endangering anyone's livelihood. Consequently, to people without a deep connection to the land, it can seem like the easiest and most equitable way to proceed.

ESTATE TAX

The purpose of the estate tax is to prevent significant capital assets from accumulating in a small number of hands over the course of generations; the underlying theory is that democracy does not function well in the presence of a permanent economic aristocracy. Just what exactly constitutes an aristocracy, however, has changed over time, with the level at which the estate tax kicks in being especially volatile in recent years. Regardless of how you feel about the estate tax, the uncertainty that springs from this volatility can be detrimental to woodland owners whose sole or primary asset is the land.

Because real estate values have appreciated quite rapidly in recent decades, many woodland owners who never thought of themselves as being wealthy might be surprised to find themselves with a taxable estate on their hands. This is exactly the type of person—someone who is land rich and cash poor—for whom the estate tax can be especially burdensome. What can happen is that the total of all the assets in the estate exceed the threshold for the exemption, and the heirs owe estate tax on the amount in excess. If the land is the primary holding, then a person's heirs might have no choice but to sell all or part of a property in order to pay the estate tax due on that very property. Suddenly, the parcelization that you wanted to avoid becomes an economic necessity for your heirs.

Estate maximum rates have been around 35 percent, which means that the heirs of a person who died in 2003 with an estate valued at $2 million would have owed $350,000 in estate taxes because $1 million of it would have exceeded the exclusion and thus been taxable. The exclusion has changed dramatically since 2000, and through 2013 the combined Gift and Estate tax exclusion is $5 million, which is making many people breathe more easily. Because estate taxes are a divisive issue, and Congress has been willing to tinker with the exclusion, it's recommended that people not assume that the $5 million exclusion will last indefinitely. As recently as 2008, the exclusion was $2 million. In 2001, it was $650,000. All of the states in the Northeast except for New Hampshire impose their own estate tax.

With some advance planning, individuals subject to the estate tax can take steps to reduce the likelihood of their heirs having to sell or subdivide the land to pay the tax bill. If the value of your estate (your land plus all other assets) is likely to be greater than $1 million or so at the time of your death, it will be well worth your time to consult with a tax attorney to investigate your options. With land routinely valued at $2,000 an acre or more, even for large parcels, 500 acres brings you to $1 million in assets on land alone. A trust, which we will discuss be-

low, might be the best way for you to keep your assets in the family.

INTRODUCTION TO ESTATE PLANNING

The words "estate planning" may make you cringe. It's okay to admit it. Nobody wants to engage in estate planning because doing so acknowledges that you aren't going to live forever. Most of us spend lots of effort avoiding that sobering reality. You also might ignore it because you think you can't possibly find yourself in a situation where your heirs would be liable for estate tax. There are two responses to that. As just noted, land and real estate have appreciated so significantly over recent decades that many more people could find their estates subject to the estate tax. Recent history of the policy debate suggests that the exclusion is likely to change, and there's no telling whether it will be increased or decreased. It seems better not to leave it to chance. Second, even though the term "estate planning" has become shorthand for figuring out ways to avoid having to pay estate taxes, it has a more universal importance than that. Estate planning is the process that culminates in decisions about the disposition of your assets, including your family forest. To do this successfully means doing it in a way that's best for the land, that you deem fair to all concerned, and that allows you to remain comfortable until you're gone. This can be tricky.

Estate planning involves creating documents (including a will) or legal entities through which you pass on your assets.

It's a very complicated affair, and you will benefit from having professional assistance as you make your decisions and work to implement them.

What are you trying to accomplish with estate planning?

- Ascertain the likelihood of estate tax liability.
- Within the limits of the law, keep as much as possible of your accumulated net worth in the family.
- Maintain good family relationships, being fully aware that the promise of wealth often brings out the worst in people. Read or go see a performance of *King Lear* if you don't understand how this works.
- Make sure that your commitment to the land is expressed clearly to your family, especially to the likely executor of your estate.
- Retain access to sufficient assets to keep you comfortable during your lifetime.

Estate planning is a process that you don't undertake alone. It will be most successful if you seek the advice of an attorney or accountant. With good advice, you will be able to make the kinds of decisions that will give you peace of mind. Just as this book can't serve as your forester or your tax accountant, neither can it be a substitute for an estate planning professional. As in the discussions of forest management and reporting timber sale income, I hope to provide you with a framework for thinking about your options that will get you moving in the right direction.

Even more important than using an estate planning professional, make sure that you include your family in the process. The time to start communicating with your family about this is now, and the best way to do it is to get the family together for a family meeting. "Oh, great," you say, an officially sanctioned family meeting, an activity most of us welcome as much as we welcome salmonella. Nonetheless, you need to overcome inertia and make plans to discuss this very important matter with your family. It's important to have the initial meeting in person.

People trained in facilitating meetings of this nature suggest that you invite all parties (including spouses), hold it in a place where everyone will be equally comfortable, and avoid the holidays because holidays can be fraught with memories, roles, pecking orders, and other family dynamics that might impede constructive discussion.

The purpose of the meeting is for everyone involved to learn as much as possible. Your heirs need to learn from you and your spouse the nature of and the potential value of your assets, as well as your commitment to the family land. You need to learn from your children or other possible heirs what the land means to them.

What you hope to learn:

- In what way and to what extent do each of your heirs value the land?
- Who has a strong attachment to it?
- Which ones see it as an asset to be cashed in rather than held?
- Which, if any, of your heirs has a particularly deep attachment to the property and could be in a position to carry on its management?

- It is assumed that a spouse is executor of a deceased spouse's estate. On the subsequent death of the surviving spouse, which of the heirs would be the most likely executor?

- What are the financial needs of your different heirs?

- If a house is part of the property, how is the house viewed? As a cherished family home full of memories? With horror, as the start of a lifetime of maintenance responsibility? A possible summer home? A place to move to in retirement? An asset to be sold?

You may learn that even though all your heirs have warm feelings toward the land and the house, none of them really wants to be responsible for the property's future care. While not what you hoped to hear, this is a valuable piece of information. Clarity like that will help you plan. Selling the property might be the best thing, since you can do so under the condition that it stay forever intact (see the section on conservation easements, below). Your heirs might be just as happy to split the money as split the land, allowing the land itself to remain whole.

In preparation for the meeting, you need to make a list of your assets and assign a value to them. Include your savings, your retirement account, stocks, insurance policies, collections of art or hand tools. Everything. Make it an annotated list, and anticipate questions your children might want to know the answers to but might feel it would be too cheeky to ask.

In particular, be free with details about your forestland. Chances are your children (maybe even your spouse) know very little about the inner workings, so you might want to prepare a booklet that includes:

- What's the land's assessed value?
- What's the value of the timber it holds?
- What are the annual property taxes?
- Is the land enrolled in the state's current use program?
- Is there a mortgage on it?
- Whose name is on the deed?
- Does it have any significant natural resources or places of particular ecological importance?
- Who is the forester?
- What does the management plan say?
- Are there zoning or other regulations that govern what can or can't happen to it?

The give and take of information might lead directly to a shared attitude toward the disposition of the land and your other assets. If so, this initial meeting may bring you to a decision and be the only one you need. Another possibility is that you'll see that further discussion of some of the pertinent details is needed. People may need time to digest all the new information before coming to a conclusion. Subsequent meetings can be held by conference call if getting together in person is a challenge for people who don't live close by.

Ultimately, you would like to reach a consensus about how the assets will be handled. Maybe you can all agree that the home place should stay in the family, and that each branch of the family should have a stake in it (more on how to do this follows below). Maybe you all agree that the house should be sold, but the rest of the land remain intact with the possibility of building a cabin or two on it. Consensus is the goal, but if after several discussions you see that there are disagreements among the heirs that can't be overcome by further discussion, that doesn't mean the process is over.

It's your decision, and you need to go ahead and make a plan even without family unity. You can't expect that the disagreements will become anything but worse if you throw up your hands and do nothing. Through the process of discussing these important matters, you've accumulated very important information. At this point, an objective estate planning professional can prove invaluable in helping you come to the right decision.

THREE TOOLS TO KEEP LAND INTACT

It would be impossible to cover all the situations that families find themselves in. Each family is different, and the increasingly common blended family just adds to the complexity. Maybe at your family meeting you ascertain that all four heirs would like to own the family forest after your death; maybe two would, and two would prefer to inherit cash. Maybe one wants to live there full-time and employ one of her grown children as property manager of a medical marijuana farm. The possibility for complications is endless.

If your goal is to ensure that your family forest remains intact, there are three primary tools that can be used together or on their own: creating a legal entity (other than yourself) to own the property; making gifts of shares of interest in the property; placing a conservation easement on the property.

DIVIDING THE OWNERSHIP, NOT THE LAND: THE LLC

If your heirs are interested in retaining ownership of the land, there is a way for you to do this that treats each heir fairly while keeping the land intact: setting up an LLC (limited liability company) to own the land. In essence, an LLC allows the ownership of a piece of land to be divided while the land itself remains intact.

Like a corporation, an LLC is a separate legal entity, but the owners are called "members" instead of "shareholders." It has the very attractive limited liability provisions of a corporation, which is preferable to a partnership, an entity in which each partner is responsible for the consequences of the other partners' actions. An LLC is less cumbersome than a C-corporation or an S-corporation. The income generated is taxed on a straight pass-through basis as if it were a partnership. In its essence, it combines the best aspects of a corporation with the best aspects of a partnership.

LLCs are relatively new legal structures that have been used in the United States only since the late 1970s. Two documents are required to legally establish an LLC: the articles of incorporation and the operating agreement. The former is filed with the secretary of state in the state where the LLC is to be based (which does not necessarily need to be the state in which the land is located), and a copy of the latter is signed and held by each of the LLC members. It is a private agreement and is not a part of the public record.

Neither document needs to be particularly complex, though each state has its own requirements. Hiring a lawyer (typical fees for establishing an LLC are on the order of a few hundred dollars) is a good way to ensure that all the bases are covered, though it's entirely possible to set up an LLC on your own, using templates and information gleaned from the internet and your secretary of state's office. Expect an annual fee and a requirement to file an annual report.

Because of the ongoing importance of the operating agreement, it probably does make sense to use the services of a lawyer in drawing it up. Lawyers routinely deal with eventualities that family members think about only in their worst nightmares. Most people would benefit from having that cold, objective perspective as they draw up documents that have such long-lasting importance.

OPERATING AGREEMENT

An LLC's operating agreement is the heart of the company as it answers all the essential questions about its purpose, how it works, who owns it and how that can change, and who makes decisions about the assets held by the company.

Let's take a look at how one landowning couple, Forrest and Sylvia Holder, established an entity called Family Forest LLC.

When they created the entity, they owned it in its entirety. They transferred ownership of their forestland by deeding it to Family Forest LLC. Since they owned the land in its entirety and the LLC in its entirety, this was a simple matter.

In developing the operating agreement, Forrest and Sylvia decided that they would each be a member, though they could have chosen to be collectively one member. In the opening paragraph of the operating agreement, they stated that the LLC's purpose is to own the land as an intact, undividable entity and to keep ownership in the family. And they stated very clearly why they have chosen to take this step to transfer ownership of the land to the LLC. They wrote: "We want our four children, and their children in turn, to own this property. It is a much more valuable forest in its undivided condition than if it were divided among the children. If at any time the decision is made to sell the property, it must be sold in its entirety." Including that statement at the outset removes any cloudiness that may develop over the generations as ownership of the company changes. Speaking of which, the Holders also stipulated that future members of the company shall be direct descendants of the founders.

The Holders learned—by hearing from each of their four children at their family meeting—that each of the children had an interest in being a part of the ownership of the land. So they made each of them members of the company. Just as corporations can have different classes of shareholders, LLCs can have different levels of ownership and responsibility. Forrest and Sylvia retain the management role in the company and make all decisions about the

setting up a trust

Trust is such a nice word that all sorts of entities have used it in their titles, which also makes it a confusing word.

There are land trusts, community housing (land) trusts, community land trusts, all of which are nonprofit entities whose missions involve community and real estate. Then there are real estate investment trusts (REITs), which are a particular type of corporation that attracts investors for real estate ventures.

The trusts we're talking about now are those formed as estate planning tools. These are freestanding entities that own assets, and they are created largely to bypass the probate process and lower estate taxes for a person's heirs. If you don't need to shield assets, you probably don't want to set up a trust. In addition to avoiding the public nature of probate court, that's their primary purpose.

Trusts can be revocable or irrevocable, or can be derived from specific parts of the United States Tax Code such as qualified personal residential trusts (QPRTs), charitable remainder trusts (CRTs), and the like. The difference between revocable and irrevocable is inherent in the terms. Once the irrevocable is signed, that's it—you've given up the right to make changes to it. Revocable means it is still under your control. Each has its benefits, and one is chosen over the other depending on the grantor's (the person setting up the trust) personal situation.

Let's say Mr. Forrest Holder sets up a trust named the Forrest Holder Revocable Trust. As the grantor, he

land. Their four children are non-voting members who will become fully vested members in a process described below.

As in any organization, it makes sense to have the decision-making authority in the hands of as few people as possible, which is why Forrest and Sylvia have structured Family Forest LLC as a manager-run company. By bringing in their four children as members at an early stage, they hope to show the four what it means to actively manage forestland. Further, Forrest and Sylvia hope that in the process it will become clear which of the four children has the most interest in and the best understanding of forest management, and can thus succeed them as the LLC's manager.

The operating agreement also spells out how income and expenses are allocated. The Holders created a company bank account in which they deposited the proceeds from a recent timber sale to cover the company's ongoing maintenance and property tax obligations. Because expenses are annual and income most likely will be sporadic, it makes sense to retain timber sale income in the company's account rather than distribute profits to members. Each year, the members will deeds his family forest to the trust. By doing so, he reduces the value of his assets to below the estate tax exclusion threshold. When Mr. Holder dies, that property will not be considered part of his estate or go through the probate court process.

The primary method for avoiding estate taxes is by reducing the value of your assets. Placing your assets in a trust separates them from you as an individual, even if you are the person who sets it up (the grantor), the person who oversees it (the trustee), and the person who benefits from the income (the beneficiary). Sounds like a neat trick, and it is. It doesn't, however, alter the fact that you're not going to live forever, so in setting up the trust, you need to name alternate beneficiaries and a successor trustee.

If you do set up a trust to own your forest, and you are committed to having it stay as a family forest, then you need to be absolutely explicit in the trust documents about the value that the land holds as an intact forest. That's because the trustee is legally bound to make the best financial decisions for the beneficiaries. Selling the land as multiple house sites may well be the way to maximize return, and a trustee would be expected to do so as it follows accepted principles of maximizing return and fiduciary responsibility.

To avoid that, state explicitly in the trust documents that you would like the trustee to place a conservation easement on the forestland that removes the development rights. Better still, donate or sell the conservation easement in your lifetime. ☉

receive a Schedule K-1 that shows their share of profits or loss from the LLC. Unless the managers decide one year to make a payout to members similar to the dividends paid to shareholders in a corporation, member profits are paper profits rather than cash. That doesn't mean they don't need to be reported to the IRS. They do, on Schedule E.

BECOMING A MEMBER

Forrest and Sylvia wanted to bring their children into the ownership as quickly as possible, so each year, the Holders trans-

fer part of the ownership in the company to their four children. The property has been appraised at $316,000. When the four children are fully vested as members, they will join their parents as members, each owning one of the six shares in the company.

The way the Holders accomplish this is through each parent making an annual gift of $13,000 worth of ownership in the LLC. Combined, the couple gives $26,000 a year to each of the four children, and after two years, each child has a share in the company worth $52,000. Transferring assets between generations via an LLC can have important tax implications for both you and your heirs, so seeking the advice of a qualified tax attorney will be well worth it. The Holders followed this process to take advantage of the IRS rules (as of 2010) that allow each parent to give gifts of up to $13,000 a year without any tax consequences for either the giver or the receiver. As long as gifts to each individual are $13,000 or less each year, the gifts are not included in the combined estate and gift tax rules.

In two years, the Holders will have reduced their assets by $208,000 by making gifts to their children, which makes good sense in their estate planning. In the process, they have brought their four children in as equal owners of Family Forest LLC. At the annual meeting of the company, they walk the forest's boundaries, discuss plans for future trails and timber sales, and revel in the pleasure of taking care of a wonderful piece of land.

While we're on the subject of gifts, there is one other type of gift that might interest those people who don't have a family member or members who would be the obvious choice to continue owning the land. If you've been particularly impressed with the work of a conservation organization, you might consider donating your land to the nonprofit organization. In this case, it's not a gift but rather a charitable contribution to a 501(c)(3) organization, and therefore the value of the gift can be taken as a deduction on Schedule A of your tax return. Unlike a gift, which has the $13,000-a-year limit, the contribution of property to a registered nonprofit can be done all at once.

Charitable contributions can offset income, so donations like this should be made when you have income to offset. In general, you can offset 30 percent of your adjusted gross income through charitable contributions, and you have six years to take the full deduction if you can't take it all at once.

It's a charitable contribution at the time you hand over complete control of the property. Some people making donations of this nature choose to retain a life estate, which means they have the right to remain in the house until death. In this arrangement, the nonprofit doesn't receive the full use of the property until your death, so you can't take the donation as a charitable contribution during your lifetime.

One other thing to consider is that you can't assume that the nonprofit will own your property for the long term and use it to conduct programs related to their mission. Unless yours is a particularly strategic property for the organization, it will more than likely sell the property and use the cash for its operations. In many cases, land that is given to an environmental organization will be conserved by that organization before they sell it. Operating funds tend to be more important than land holdings.

CONSERVATION EASEMENTS

In the world of forestry and conservation, one of the most significant developments in the last three decades has been the steadily increasing use of conservation easements. Through a process in which a landowner transfers the property's development rights either by selling or donating those rights to a land trust, millions of acres have been conserved. Much of the early work in this field was to conserve family farms that were ripe targets for developers, but recently the largest conserved holdings have been forestland. Working-forest easements ensure that the land will never be developed for housing and that it will continue to be managed for the production of forest products according to the principles of sound forestry.

Land trusts range from large organizations that work in more than one state to small local outfits formed with a specific project in mind. With a rallying cry of "Save Woodchuck Mountain," neighbors concerned about development of a local landmark find themselves charter board members of a local land trust. The Land Trust Alliance, a national association, estimates that there are more than 1,700 nonprofit land trusts operating in the United States.

Essential to the concept of conservation easements is what has come to be known as the bundle of rights. When you own land and have all the rights intact, you are said to have fee simple title to it. You own the rights to use it however you like, as long as it's in accord with local, state, and federal law. You own the right to sell part or all of it, to build on it, to improve access into it. You own the right to harvest trees, drill a well, and to extract minerals. One simple way in which you might give up or sell part of your bundle of rights is if you have granted the power company an easement for its power line to run through it. You have given it the right

to use that land for that purpose, and it's written into your deed. When you sell the land, that easement runs with the land. In other words, the buyer is obligated in the same way you were.

It's the same with development rights. You can sell or grant the right to develop the property. Most often this right is transferred to a land trust that was formed to hold such rights in perpetuity, but sometimes, the development rights are held by the state or federal government.

If you own prime agricultural land that is highly developable, or have 500 or more acres of forestland, it's possible that a land trust may be interested in purchasing your development rights. It all depends on the parcel's location and desirability, and the availability of funds. An appraiser would do what amounts to two appraisals. The first appraisal would estimate the fair market value of your land with the development rights intact, the second with your development rights removed and owned by the land trust. It's a complicated calculation, and it relies in part on sales of comparable properties, which might not be that easy to come by. The difference between the two appraisals is the value of the development rights. Maybe the land trust will offer full price for your development rights. More likely, you would be asked to sell the rights for less than full value, which is known as a bargain sale.

If your family forest is a couple hundred acres or less, a land trust is not likely to buy your development rights (unless you're in a densely settled area and your land is the last remnant of natural forest), but they might be interested in accepting your donation of those rights. It works the same way: the before and after appraisals would be done, and the value of your gift is the difference between the two prices. You can deduct the value of this gift on Schedule A of your income tax return. As noted above, there are restrictions on how much you can deduct for charitable donations in any one year. These restrictions have been known to change, but in recent years, you could deduct up to 50 percent of your adjusted gross income in the year of your gift, and you may carry over any unused deduction for up to 15 years.

On the cost side of the equation, there are considerable expenses incurred by the land trust that you probably will be asked to cover. If the land is not already surveyed, that can add considerable expenses. In addition, the land trust is likely to urge you to make a contribution to what's known as a stewardship endowment. Plus, you will have your own legal costs. All these expenses may seem counterintuitive: you are being magnanimous and giving them something of real value; isn't that enough? Why would you have to pay extra for the opportunity to make this donation?

When you think about what they are agreeing to do, however, you will recognize that it's quite a costly obligation on their part to monitor the terms of your gift in perpetuity. The land trust needs to maintain sufficient staff to visit every one of their easements each year to make sure that structures haven't been built, roads put in, or any of the other forms of development undertaken that are banned by the agreement. If you sell the land, which you of course have retained the right to do, it will be sold without the development rights, and the new owners are bound by the same conditions that you have been. They must abide by the agreement you've made, as must the party they sell it to. Perpetuity is a long time, and it's the land trust's responsibility to visit the land to ensure that the owners are abiding by the conditions.

The common expression used for donating a property's development rights is placing a conservation easement on it. In Massachusetts, it's known as a conservation restriction. Because the words easement and restriction aren't all that friendly, some people are now calling it a conservation agreement. It's all the same thing: the development rights are separated from the rest of the bundle of rights. Because the land trust is in the business of conserving land, it is assumed that they will never exercise the right to develop the land, though we need to be clear that the development rights aren't officially extinguished. They are just held by an organization whose charter states that it won't exercise the rights; the charter also makes provisions for assigning its assets to another land trust in the event it ceases operations.

Under a conservation agreement, land trusts don't end up owning the land; they just hold the development rights. You retain the right to sell or bequeath the land just as before, and you can transfer ownership of the land to your LLC. Figuring out the best strategy and the sequence—does the conservation agreement precede the transfer to the LLC, or vice versa?—may require the help of an attorney.

You may ask, wouldn't it be easier and less expensive to take care of long-term conservation through deed restrictions or mutual covenants? Couldn't you just state in your deed that the new owner can only build one more house and that it can only be built near the blacktop and existing utilities and not on the ridgeline?

Less expensive, yes. But less effective as well. Deed restrictions are fairly common, but the difference between a deed restriction and a conservation easement is that enforcement of the former is left to the land's owners. There is no land trust keeping track of the details, and nobody making sure that the deed restrictions are followed. This may not seem like a problem right away, when your heirs and neighbors know what it is that you intended, but the deed details could easily be forgotten a few decades hence when none of the original parties to the deed restriction remain on the scene. If Forrest and Sylvia want to guarantee that the family forest owned by Family Forest LLC remains intact, they should not rely on the clear instruction in their operating agreement but should instead conserve the property.

A second problem with deed restrictions is that they are potentially reversible. Let's say you carve a roadside lot off your larger holding, keeping a deed-restricted right-of-way to the back lot to ensure that forest management can always take place there. In the future, however, if someone ended up owning both the front lot and the back lot, they would control both halves of the deed restriction and could decide to extinguish it. With no third party (such as a land trust)

having legal standing, your intentions would be overturned.

Many conservation agreements are done with the recognition that the current land management practices will continue. Some land trusts are very amenable to working-forest agreements; they understand that managing land for forest products helps to pay some of the costs of owning land, and they are in philosophical agreement with the concept of working land. They will have their own standards for management plans, but you can have them look at your current plan to see if it fits their philosophy. If they have reservations about the management plan you have worked out with your forester, then perhaps you should look for another land trust.

Some land trusts, however, are more interested in the preservation of open space than in the working landscape. It's important to find the right fit if your interests are to be protected into the future By entering into this agreement, you are ceding certain rights and retaining others, and the closer your philosophy of land use coincides with the land trust's, the better off you will be.

When working with a land trust, it's important to retain a healthy skepticism and a strong interest in self-preservation. Your interests and those of the land trust are similar in that you both want to protect and create a bright future for the land that means so much to you. Despite all the wonderful warm feelings these shared interests engender, be prepared to negotiate with a sober understanding that a grantor and a grantee have different needs and goals. Land trusts are well-equipped to look out for their own interest in negotiating the deed. Presumably, you are not as well-equipped when you enter the discussion, so getting advice and reading up are crucial. It's not that you are adversaries—it's just that your needs are somewhat different from theirs. You'll benefit from retaining the services of an attorney who specializes in conservation easements.

Pay attention to the draft of the deed—yes, the conservation agreement is a legal deed—that's presented to you and be ready to negotiate its terms. Elements typical of today's easement deeds include purposes, affirmative rights (what you expressly can do), restrictions (what you can't do), reserved rights, and terms and conditions. Watch out for your own interests and those of your heirs in order to have a successful outcome. You can often negotiate, for instance, for an excluded area that can be separated from the rest of the land, for the right to build one more house, to dig a pond, or to build a camp up in the back corner.

There's one more important caveat. Do your research and carefully evaluate your own circumstances before assuming you'll receive any property tax benefits from ceding the development rights to the land.

Experience shows that your property tax is unlikely to be reduced, even though the fair market value of the land will have decreased. Although the reduced value can be demonstrated clearly through the appraisal, it's by no means a given that your town will reduce its assessment of the property.

On the other hand, the value of your estate will be reduced, which may have further implications. Regarding income tax, you should consider carefully whether the timing is right for you to donate development rights. The best time to sell an easement is when you most need the money. The best financial time to donate an easement is when your income is the highest.

In summary, it's possible for you to have your land and conserve it, too. Parcelization and fragmentation are serious problems that can be avoided with advanced planning. Conservation easements can be undertaken at any time, as can the transition to LLC ownership and estate-tax planning. Your heirs can benefit from your long-time commitment to good forestry without having to forgo their inheritance. The best time to start thinking about all these options is now. ◘

CONCLUSION

The process of writing a book is one of crystallizing thoughts. As I've worked on this project, two of the ideas central to it came into ever sharper focus. The first has to do with the significance of the origins of forestry. It was born in a Europe that had been settled for thousands of years, where forests had given way to farmland and occupied a much smaller portion of the land than they had before the arrival of people.

As populations grew, land became increasingly precious, and an agricultural mindset was applied to every acre—even the forests. Forestry developed as a means of getting the most production possible without compromising the land's capacity to keep yielding wood.

A hundred or so years ago, that model came to the United States intact, largely through the work of Gifford Pinchot. It proved to be workable and appropriate for much of the land, especially the large tracts. But times have changed, and the owners of forestland in the Northeast tend to think along different lines these days. The traditional agrarian approach to forests has given way to one that's more natural. Maintaining wildland and work-ing with the natural system are now the hallmarks of forestry as it's practiced in family forests in the Northeast.

That is closely related to the second central idea, that you can't separate the natural world from the human world. Humans are part of nature, and we have had a huge influence on it. In the years leading up to the mid-nineteenth century, we cleared millions of acres to tame the land and grow food. Then, having found more easily farmed land to the west, we let a large percentage of the Northeast's farmland grow back to forests. In clearing and then abandoning the farms, we dramatically altered the natural plant and animal communities.

Most people are aware of the scale of our impact. That understanding shouldn't lead, however, to an attempt to keep our hands off and somehow enshrine nature. That would be impossible because all that we need in our daily lives—food, shelter, heat, water, and materials for commerce—comes from the land.

This book attempts to show how people can interact with the forested environment in ways that are at least benign, and maybe even beneficial. When we remove resources from their natural environment for our use, we are changing what was there. If we pay attention to and act with kind regard for the nearly miraculous assemblage of organisms that inhabit our woods, we can lighten our impact.

There are few things more satisfying in life than growing your own food or building your own house. To those elemental activities, I would add tending your own forestland. I hope this book inspires you to manage your woods with care and with pleasure so that you can get the most from your family forest.

Enough words. Let's all head out to the woods for a nice long walk. ▣

TIMBER SALE CONTRACT

Before having any cutting done in your woods, make sure you have a signed contract that spells out all the details—and there are lots of details. Here is a sample contract that should give you an idea of what needs to be agreed upon beforehand.

TIMBER SALE CONTRACT

This contract is made between Forrest Holder, hereinafter called the Landowners, and Careful Cutter, hereinafter called the Logger, this 26th day of August, 20__.

Long-Term Forestry, hereinafter called the Forester, will act as agent for the Landowners and administer this timber sale. Any questions regarding operations will be directed to them.

The Landowners agree to permit access and to sell, and the Logger agrees to purchase standing trees on the Landowners' property in Oakwood Corner, Vermont. The timber sale is subject to the following terms:

1. All trees and only those trees that are marked with blue paint at approximately 4.5 feet above the ground and at the base shall be cut. All trees cut by the Logger that have not been marked or designated for cutting by the Landowners or Forester will be paid for at three times the rates specified in Item 7 of this contract, unless they are removed for the construction of normal and reasonable skid trails with approval of Forester. Trees marked with a long vertical stripe or marked trees less than 7 inches in diameter are considered pre-commercial. At his choice, the Logger can cut and leave these trees, but is not required to harvest them. These trees have been marked to help the Logger make skidding and felling decisions. Trees marked with an "X" have been "unmarked" and should be left.

2. All trees that are cut shall be put into the maximum value product obtainable.

3. The Landowners warrant that there are no mortgages or encumbrances affecting the sale of the timber covered by this contract.

4. The Landowners warrant that the title of the marked and designated timber is guaranteed to the Logger, and the Landowners will do nothing during the term of this contract to interfere with or jeopardize the rights of the Logger to said marked or designated timber.

5. The Landowners warrant that the property lines necessary for this sale are clearly and correctly marked.

6. In the event that the Logger fails to fulfill any of the terms of this contract, the Forester or the Landowners, upon written notice to the Logger, shall have the right to stop further cutting by the Logger, and title to cut, marked, or designated timber shall immediately revert to the Landowners and the Logger's rights under this Contract shall be automatically terminated.

7. The Logger will pay the Landowners for standing trees as follows:

Pulp and firewood	$8/Cord
Sawlogs: Mill price	Stumpage rate
$150/MBF or less	$10
$151–250/MBF	25%
$251–550/MBF	33%
$551–1,000/MBF	50%
Greater than $1,000/MBF	65%

It is understood that the cost of trucking shall be paid by the Logger.

8. Payment for all timber shall be made in the form of a check made out to the Landowners and mailed to the Forester no later than 30 days after timber left the landing.

A mill-tally slip or scale sheet from the mill will accompany payment.

9. The Logger agrees to save the Landowners and Forester harmless from any and all claims for injury or damage to persons or property resulting from the acts or omissions of the Logger, his agents, employees, or others under his control during the period of this contract.

10. The Landowners and/or Forester reserve the right to cancel this contract or suspend operations if this contract is breached. If the contract is canceled the Logger will remove all equipment within five days of written notice and leave landings and access roads in satisfactory condition.

11. The Landowners shall indemnify the Logger against all liability on account of any action for trespass as long as the Logger shall limit his logging operations to the confines of the stands designated by the Landowners.

12. The Logger shall not fell any trees over the boundary line or cross the boundary line with any equipment, and shall be responsible for any expenses incurred due to failure of the Logger to comply fully with this contract.

13. All trees shall be cut as close to the ground as possible.

14. Care shall be taken to protect all young trees and other trees that are not cut. All roads and landings shall be left in a satisfactory

condition, smoothed over and waterbarred. The entrance shall be obstructed to prevent unauthorized use of the woods roads before the soil has settled.

15. The Logger shall take special care to construct skid roads in a manner that will minimize the possibility of sediment reaching any stream or body of water. All roads shall be left in proper repair, as approved by the Forester, upon completion of the logging.

16. Title to cut timber shall pass to the Logger at the time the wood leaves the landing.

17. No trash shall be left on the land during or following logging. No oil, grease, or fuel shall be drained on the ground. Equipment leaking oil product shall be repaired or removed from the premises.

18. All water courses shall be bridged or culverts shall be installed and all slash shall be removed from all water courses by the completion of the job.

19. The Logger agrees to observe all town, state, and federal laws and to use precautions to prevent forest fires. The Logger takes full responsibility for adhering to best management practices (BMPs) throughout the term of this contract.

20. At log landing and loading areas, all forms of waste, including unmerchantable logs or portions of logs, shall either be trucked away, returned to woods, buried, or pushed to a designated location per the instructions of the Forester. The landing areas should then be smoothed and leveled to conform to the original topography and seeded when necessary as approved by the Forester. Hay bales and/ or annual grass seed, if necessary for erosion control, will be paid for and applied by the Logger.

21. This contract may not be assigned, transferred, sold, or made over to any other party without prior written permission from the Landowners.

22. The terms of this sale are completely set forth in this contract and none of its terms may be varied or modified except in writing by both parties of this contract.

23. The Forester may suspend removal operations if the Forester determines that unreasonable damage to access roads, skid roads, or logging roads is resulting from the use of these roads during periods of excessive wetness.

24. The Logger shall post a cash or surety bond of $3,000, to be held by the Forester. Said bond will be returned at the completion of this contract. In the event of damage to residual timber or unclean landing area, non-payment or breach of any part of this contract, it will be retained in part or in whole to be applied to any clean-up activity or damages the Landowners suffer under the terms of this contract.

25. The Logger shall work as steadily as possible until the job is completed.

26. The Logger shall maintain General Liability Insurance, in the amount of $_____ throughout the term of this contract. The Logger shall furnish proof of such insurance to the Forester and the Landowners prior to the commencement of any work.

This contract shall begin on the date of signature and shall terminate on the 1st day of January, 20__. This contract may be extended if necessary and agreed upon, in writing, by the Landowners and the Logger.

This contract shall be binding upon the heirs, executors, administrators, successors, and assigns of the parties hereto.

SIGNATURES

_____   _____
Landowner   *Date*

_____   _____
Witness   *Date*

_____   _____
Logger   *Date*

_____   _____
Witness   *Date*

GLOSSARY

acre   An area that contains 43,560 square feet.

advanced regeneration   Seedlings and saplings that have become established before the existing overstory is removed.

aspect   The compass direction toward which a slope faces.

BMPs   Best management practices. In logging operations, the term most commonly refers to those practices recommended for maintaining water quality during and after the job. Sometimes these guidelines are called AMPs—acceptable management practices.

basal area   The cross-sectional area of a tree trunk 4½ feet above the ground. Basal area per acre is the sum of the basal areas of the trees greater than 5 inches in diameter on an acre; it is used as a measure of forest density.

biomass   Whole trees or parts of trees that are chipped and used for producing heat, electricity, or both.

board foot   A unit for measuring wood volume in a tree, log, or board. A board foot is commonly 1 foot by 1 foot by 1 inch, but any shape containing 144 cubic inches of wood equals one board foot.

bole   The trunk of a tree.

browse   Parts of woody plants, including twigs, shoots, and leaves, eaten by animals.

buck   To cut trees into shorter lengths such as logs or cordwood.

buffer strip   A vegetated area of undisturbed ground adjacent to a watercourse or other wet or sensitive area.

bumper trees   Trees along a skid trail whose trunks are marred by trees as they are skidded by. They are often left in place after the job on the assumption that the same trails will be used for a future logging operation.

canopy   The cover formed by tree crowns in a forest.

carbon sequestration   The process through which carbon dioxide is removed from the atmosphere and stored for a significant amount of time as carbon in oceans, forests, or other carbon sinks.

cavity tree   A tree in which woodpeckers have excavated nesting holes in diseased wood. Many species of birds and mammals then use the cavities in subsequent years for nesting.

clearcut   The harvest of all the trees in an area. When used as a regeneration harvest, any advanced regeneration of desirable species is left standing.

cogeneration   Means of energy production in which biomass is burned to simultaneously generate electricity and provide heat to nearby buildings.

cohort   Trees that are considered to be the same age for forest management purposes. The difference in age between the oldest and youngest trees in a cohort is less than 20 years.

commercial clearcut   A harvest in which all merchantable timber is removed.

conservation easement   Sometimes known as a conservation restriction or a conservation agreement, it restricts the permissible activities on a piece of property. Commonly used to restrict residential or commercial development on land that is productive for agriculture or forestry, these easements are filed as deeds and hold all future owners to the same conditions.

consulting forester   A forester with the training and experience to assist forest owners in managing their land.

cord   A measurement of wood that is equal to a stack 4 x 4 x 8 feet or 128 cubic feet.

crop tree   Tree that has desirable characteristics that make it worth retaining so it can increase in value. That value is most often, but not always, commercial.

crown   The live branches and foliage of a tree.

cruise   A forest inventory used to obtain information about tree size, species, and value.

cull   A tree large enough to be sawtimber but lacking timber value as a result of poor shape or damage from injury, insects, or disease.

cutting cycle   The period of time between harvesting operations in an uneven-aged or even-aged stand.

DBH   Diameter at breast height, the standard measurement of a tree's diameter, taken at 4½ feet above the ground.

deeryards   Deer wintering areas, in which deer are protected from harsh winter conditions. They feature dense stands of conifers, with hemlock and cedar providing the best protection.

density   The quantity of trees in an area, usually evaluated in terms of basal area per acre, which takes both tree size and number of trees into account.

diameter   See *DBH*.

disturbance   An event or condition that leads to the death of trees, either singly, in groups, or across an entire stand.

early successional species   An association of both herbaceous and woody plants capable of occupying an area after a major disturbance.

epicormic branch   A branch that grows on the stem of a tree from a bud produced under the bark rather than from the tree's core. Severe epicormic branching reduces lumber quality.

even-aged management   A silvicultural system in which a stand of trees is grown to a rotation age, from inception to maturity, at which time a new cohort becomes established.

even-aged stand   A stand in which most of the trees are within a decade or two of being the same age. It can include one other age cohort, but for most of the stand's life, it's limited to one. The second cohort would consist of regenerating trees.

feller-buncher   A mechanical harvester, with which the operator fells trees and bunches them for a grapple skidder to transport to a landing.

forest type   A natural association of tree species that commonly occur together. Spruce-fir and hemlock-hardwoods are examples.

forester   A person with a college-level degree in forestry and experience in managing forests. In some states, but not all, foresters need to obtain a license to practice.

forwarder   Equipment used to transport trees by carrying them in a bunk. They can ride either on tracks or large tires designed to reduce damage to the ground.

group selection   The practice of harvesting groups of trees within an uneven-aged stand. The resulting openings—generally between ½ acre and 2 acres in size—provide space within which new trees can become established.

harvester, cut-to-length (CTL)   A mechanical harvester with which the operator can fell trees and then buck them to specific log lengths.

heartwood   The older, nonliving central wood of a tree or woody plant, usually darker and harder than the younger sapwood that surrounds it.

hectare   An area containing 10,000 square meters or 2.47 acres.

high-grading   A harvest in which the most valuable timber is removed, leaving behind small, suppressed, and poorly formed trees and less valuable species.

hitch   The clutch of logs that constitute the payload of a cable or grapple skidder.

horizontal diversity   The complexity of the arrangement of trees and shrubs in a forest, most noticeable as variation in density and size of stems.

humus   Humus consists of the long-lasting remains of decayed organic material. It holds water and improves soil structure.

intermediate treatments   Any harvests that are carried out after regeneration is established and before the final removal of the overstory. In general, it refers to thinning and other harvests designed to improve the growing stock.

intolerant species   Those tree species that can't reproduce in shade.

irregular shelterwood harvest   A variation on a shelterwood cut that can be used to convert an even-aged stand to uneven-aged.

landing   A cleared area within a timber harvest where harvested logs are processed, piled, and loaded for transport to a sawmill or other facility. Also known as a header or yard.

late-successional community   The culmination of a succession cycle, marked by the presence of large, mature specimens of long-lived, shade-tolerant species such as sugar maple, American beech, eastern hemlock, or red spruce.

log rule   Any of several different scales used to measure the number of board feet in a log.

logger   The person who fells the trees, transports them to the landing, and arranges to have them delivered to buyers.

lump-sum sale   A timber sale in which an agreed-on price for marked standing trees is set before the wood is removed (as opposed to a unit sale).

mast   Tree nuts and seeds, such as acorns, beechnuts, and chestnuts, that serve as food for wildlife, are hard mast. Apples, cherries, and other fruits are known as soft mast.

MBF   Abbreviation for 1,000 board feet.

mill-tally sale   Also known as pay-as-cut, unit-priced, or mill-delivered. A type of timber sale in which the wood is sold based on the volume sold to mills or intermediate buyers.

mosaic stand   A forest stand with significant variability (patchiness). The patchiness could be expressed in the tree species distribution or, most likely, the stand structure, that is, whether it's even-aged or uneven-aged.

natural community   An interacting assemblage of organisms, their physical environment, and the natural processes that affect them.

old growth   A forest that has had the chance to develop for centuries without direct intervention or manipulation by humans.

overstory   The level of forest canopy that includes the crowns of dominant, co-dominant, and intermediate trees.

patch cut   A clearcut, but one that removes all the trees from only a section or sections of a stand.

pioneer species   Species such as aspen and paper birch that are quick to become established and grow on disturbed ground.

pith   The small, soft, spongy central column of a tree.

pole timber   A size class designating trees that are between 5 and 10 inches in diameter.

pre-commercial thinning   An improvement cut that weeds out trees of poor quality. The trees cut are not removed and do not produce any revenue.

prescription   A recipe for a silvicultural treatment.

prism   A wedge of glass used to determine the basal area of a stand by identifying count trees based on size and proximity to the prism.

pulpwood   Wood processed to make pulp for paper products.

q-factor   A mathematical formula for determining the relative distribution of tree diameters in an uneven-aged stand.

regeneration   New trees, or the process by which new trees are established in a forest. New growth may come from seeds or seedlings, or from stump sprouts or root suckers.

regeneration harvest   A timber harvest designed to promote establishment of a new stand, either by natural regeneration or by planting. Clear-cuts, shelterwood, and seed tree are even-aged regeneration harvests. Group selection is an uneven-aged regeneration harvest.

release   The cutting of adjacent trees that are impeding the growth of favored trees.

residual stand   The trees left standing after a timber harvest is completed.

riparian zone   The transitional area between a waterbody and upland habitats.

rotation   The number of years required to grow an even-aged stand from establishment to final harvest.

sapling   A tree at least 4½ feet tall and up to 4 inches in diameter.

sapwood   The outer wood lying between the cambium and the heartwood of any woody plant. It is active in water conduction and it is usually lighter in color than the heartwood.

sawtimber   A tree at least 11 inches DBH that is suitable for conversion to lumber.

scarification   Preparation of a seedbed for trees by exposing the mineral soil.

seed tree harvest   A harvest where only scattered mature trees are left standing as a seed source for the next generation of trees. These "seed trees" are normally harvested once the regeneration is well established.

seedling   A tree less than 2 inches in diameter at breast height that has grown from a seed rather than from a sprout.

selection harvest   The periodic harvest of individual trees or small groups of trees of all ages and sizes to maintain an uneven-aged forest. Selection harvests are most commonly used to favor shade-tolerant species.

shade tolerance   The capacity of trees to thrive in shaded conditions. Sugar maple and eastern hemlock are known for their shade tolerance; paper birch and aspen are intolerant of shade.

shelterwood harvest   The harvest of all mature trees in an area in a series of two or more cuts, intended to create appropriate light conditions for establishment of a new stand that includes some shade-intolerant species. Enough large trees are retained to partially shade the forest floor (and sometimes as a seed source) until regeneration is well established, at which time the final harvest takes place.

single-tree selection   A technique used in uneven-aged management where individual trees are selected for harvest. Trees of all ages and sizes are typically removed, with the makeup of the future forest the primary consideration. Note the difference between this and *thinning*.

site   The combination of biotic, climatic, topographic, and soil conditions of an area.

site index   A measure of the quality of a site based on the height of dominant trees at a specified age (usually 25 or 50 years), depending on the species.

skid trail   The path through the woods that the skidder uses to bring felled trees to the landing.

skidder   A rubber-tired machine with a cable winch or grapple used to drag logs out of the forest.

slash   Branches and other woody material left in the woods after logging.

snag   A dead tree that is still standing. Snags provide important food and cover for a wide variety of wildlife species.

stand   A group of forest trees of sufficiently uniform species composition, age, and condition to be considered a homogeneous unit for management purposes.

stems per acre   The number of trees greater than 5 inches per acre, usually arrived at through statistical sampling.

stocking   The density of trees in a forest stand. Stands are often classified as *understocked*, *well-stocked*, or *overstocked*.

structure   Forest structure is the variety and arrangement of trees, both living and dead, standing and downed. It's useful to think of it as the combination of the vertical and horizontal.

stumpage   The price paid for standing forest trees.

succession   The natural replacement of one plant community by another over time in the absence of significant disturbance.

sustained yield   An ideal forest management objective in which the volume of wood removed over time is less than the growth within the total forest.

thinning   A technique used in even-aged management. Some trees are harvested or otherwise killed (by cutting and leaving, girdling, or using chemicals) from an overstocked stand of trees so that the remaining trees will have more access to resources (light, water, nutrients) and grow faster. Primary considerations in thinning are the tree crown spacing and retaining the trees of best form and of desirable species.

timber cruise   See *cruise*.

timber stand improvement (TSI)   Any practice that increases the value or rate of value growth in a stand of potential sawtimber trees. Pruning and thinning are considered TSI.

tolerance   Often referred to as shade tolerance, it refers to a tree species' capacity to become established, survive, and grow in shade. Many shade-tolerant species can survive for decades as seedlings in fairly deep shade and then respond with rapid growth when more light reaches them when the overstory is harvested, dies, or is severely damaged.

understory   The level of forest vegetation beneath the canopy.

uneven-aged management   A silvicultural system used to maintain a condition in which trees of at least three different ages are present.

uneven-aged stand   An area of forest with trees of at least three distinct age classes; also called an all-aged stand.

veneer   Thin sheets of wood made from large, straight, uniform trees. It also refers to the trees that provide this product.

vertical diversity   A forest that has leafy vegetation at different heights —including the shrub layer, midstory, and canopy—is said to be vertically diverse.

wetland   An area that is saturated or inundated with water during the growing season, with soils that have developed in saturated conditions, and vegetation well-adapted to saturated soils.

wildlife habitat   The arrangement of sources of food, water, and cover needed by a particular species.

RESOURCES FOR LANDOWNERS

BOOKS

New England Wildlife: Habitat, Natural History, and Distribution
Richard M. DeGraaf and Mariko Yamasaki

Technical Guide to Forest Wildlife Habitat Management in New England
Richard M. DeGraaf, Mariko Yamasaki, and William B. Leak

Wetland, Woodland, Wildland: A Guide to the Natural Communities of Vermont
Elizabeth H. Thompson and Eric R. Sorenson

The Nature of New Hampshire: Natural Communities of the Granite State
Dan Sperduto and Ben Kimball

Natural Landscapes of Maine: A Guide to Natural Communities and Ecosystems
Susan Gawler and Andrew Cutko

Reading the Forested Landscape: A Natural History of New England
Tom Wessels

The Trees in My Forest
Bernd Heinrich

Thoreau's Country: Journey through a Transformed Landscape
David Foster

Changes in the Land: Indians, Colonists, and the Ecology of New England
William Cronon

Legal Aspects of Owning and Managing Woodlands
Thom McEvoy

Working with Your Woodland: A Landowner's Guide
Mollie Beattie, Charles Thompson, and Lynn Levine

Woodlot Management Handbook
Stewart Hilts and Peter Mitchell

Good Forestry in the Granite State
UNH Cooperative Extension

Biodiversity in the Forests of Maine
Gro Flatebo, Carol Foss, and Steven Pelletier

The Landowner's Guide to Conservation Easements
Steven Bick and Harry L. Haney, Jr.

Trees of New England: A Natural History
Charles Fergus

Mammal Tracks and Sign: A Guide to North American Species
Mark Elbroch

Forest Forensics: A Field Guide to Reading the Forested Landscape
Tom Wessels

Naturally Curious: A Photographic Field Guide and Month-by-Month Journey through the Fields, Woods, and Marshes of New England
Mary Holland

Mushrooms and Other Fungi of North America
Roger Phillips

Newcomb's Wildflower Guide
Lawrence Newcomb

The Sibley Field Guide to Birds of Eastern North America
David Sibley

MAGAZINES

Northern Woodlands

Northern Logger

Independent Sawmill & Woodlot Management

WEBSITES

WEBINARS AND FORESTRY FORUM

ForestConnect, Cornell Cooperative Extension, www.forestconnect.com

FORESTRY AND SILVICULTURE

Be Woods Wise, Department of Conservation, Maine Forest Service www.maine.gov/doc/mfs/woodswise/

Silvics of North America, Forest Service, United States Department of Agriculture www.na.fs.fed.us/spfo/pubs/silvics_manual/table_of_contents.htm

Vermont Family Forests www.familyforests.org

Foresters for the Birds http://vt.audubon.org/fbi.html#bird

Northern Woodlands www.northernwoodlands.org (includes state-specific landowner guides)

Good Forestry in the Granite State N.H. Department of Resources and Economic Development, Division of Forests and Lands, UNH Cooperative Extension, and The Society for the Protection of NH Forests http://extension.unh.edu/goodforestry/index.htm

FOREST CERTIFICATION

Forest Stewardship Council www.fsc.org

Sustainable Forestry Initiative www.sfiprogram.org

TAXES

National Timber Tax Website www.timbertax.org

LANDOWNER ASSOCIATIONS

Vermont Woodlands Association

New Hampshire Timberland Owners Association

New York Forest Owners Association

Small Woodland Owners Association of Maine

Massachusetts Forest Landowners Association

Catskill Forest Association

Catskill Landowners Association

New England Forestry Foundation

Tree Farm program in each state

COVERTS PROGRAMS
(wildlife habitat programs for landowners)

Connecticut Coverts

Keystone Project (Massachusetts)

Master Forest Owners (New York)

New Hampshire Coverts

Rhode Island Coverts

Vermont Coverts

EXTENSION PROGRAMS

Cornell University Cooperative Extension

University of Connecticut Cooperative Extension

University of Maine Cooperative Extension

University of Massachusetts-Amherst Cooperative Extension

University of New Hampshire Cooperative Extension

University of Rhode Island Cooperative Extension

University of Vermont Cooperative Extension

GOVERNMENT FORESTERS

Connecticut Division of Forestry in the Department of Environmental Protection

Maine Forest Service in the Department of Conservation

Massachusetts Bureau of Forestry in the Department of Conservation and Recreation

New Hampshire Division of Forests and Lands in the Department of Resources and Economic Development

New York Lands and Waters Division of the Department of Environmental Conservation

Rhode Island Division of Forest Environment in the Bureau of Natural Resources

Vermont Forestry Division of the Department of Forests, Parks and Recreation

OTHER GOVERNMENT AGENCIES

Natural Resource Conservation Service in each state

U.S.D.A. Forest Service Northern Research Station in Durham, New Hampshire

FORESTER ASSOCIATIONS

Association of Consulting
Foresters of America, Inc.

New England Society of
American Foresters

New York Society of American Foresters

The Forest Guild

LAND TRUSTS

Check the website of the Land Trust
Alliance to find a land trust near you:
www.landtrustalliance.org

INDEX

Notes: Page numbers for glossary terms appear in **bold** type. An *f* following a page number indicates a *figure* (picture, drawing, or table).

ACKNOWLEDGMENTS

The five writers who worked with me on this book are individually and collectively a tremendous wealth of information about forests.

You won't see their bylines on particular chapters, but they have each influenced this book tremendously, both through writing original drafts and by helping me shape later drafts. It's an honor to be in their company. Michael Snyder is an articulate and passionate voice for good forestry, and his role as commissioner of Vermont's Department of Forests, Parks, and Recreation makes good use of his many talents. Irwin Post brings an engineer's precision, a commitment to excellence, and a lifetime of woods-based experience to all of his writing. I always count on Charlie Thompson to provide a slightly different perspective on all things related to forest management, and his insights invariably lead to a more thorough and thoughtful examination of the subject. Each of these foresters has written for *Northern Woodlands* magazine, and it's always a pleasure to work with them, which is why I wanted them to be involved in this book. The other two contributors are long-time colleagues from my years at *Northern Woodlands*. Chuck Wooster shares the distinction with me of being the only other non-forester on the team. He brings editorial skills, a gift for taking on a wide mix of responsibilities, and his perspective as a landowner who manages both farm and forest as a business. Virginia Barlow was my partner in founding *Northern Woodlands*, and is the person most responsible for my forestry education. Her love of all woodland creatures—particularly the unappealing ones—has inspired me to keep my eyes and my mind open.

It was a great pleasure working with Joe Smith on the illustrations. A forester and artist, Joe was the perfect illustrator for the job. Jenna Dixon, the book's designer, is resourceful, creative, and organized—a wonderful combination of traits.

All writers benefit from manuscript readers who know something about the subject matter and about the written word. I thank two dedicated stewards of forestland, each of them with an editorial background: John Sullivan of Chestertown, New York, and Ann Davis of Wilmot, New Hampshire. Their suggestions and observations have made this a better book.

Thanks also to Michael Jurnak, a CPA with Berry Dunn in Manchester, New Hampshire, whose knowledge of the tax code helped clarify the information in the chapter on timber taxes.

Mary Hays is my favorite writer—and my wife—and I always follow her suggestions for improving my prose. She read the manuscript in its final stages, as did Sue Kashanski, another *Northern Woodlands* alum. In copyediting the manuscript, Sue saved me from making a number of errors that would have been oh, so embarrassing. The errors that remain are my responsibility alone.

Along the way, I turned to a number of people with questions. David Paganelli is the county forester in our county in Vermont, and he introduced me to forest management and enrolled me in the current use program twenty years ago. We've walked in my woods many times, and he always asks challenging questions that help me understand more of the implications of my management choices. Markus Bradley at Redstart Forestry is my consulting forester, and I've learned much about the complexity of forestry decisions by marking trees with him on my land for timber sales. Thanks also go to him for providing a template for the timber sale contract. Paul Harwood is a consulting for-ester who explains complex concepts very well. Audubon Vermont's Steve Hagenbuch helped me understand songbird habitat. Annette Lorraine, a Montpelier, Vermont, attorney with a specialty in conservation, patiently explained the complications of trusts and conservation easements.

It takes money to publish a book, and we have been blessed to have had crucial backing while the book was in the development stage. We gratefully acknowledge a major gift from Barbara D. and David M. Roby and a grant from the Northeast State Foresters Association (NEFA). As the book has been brought to publication, we have benefited from grants from Riverledge Foundation, Plum Creek Foundation, and the Vermont Department of Forests, Parks, and Recreation. Thanks to all for your confidence and your support.

This book was developed over many years, throughout which I was employed by Northern Woodlands. The organization's commitment to this project gave me the gift of time to nurture it while juggling my other responsibilities. The final stage of this book was completed while I was a Bullard Fellow at Harvard Forest in Petersham, Massachusetts. I am grateful to both organizations for making it possible to bring this book to print.

—*Stephen Long*

ABOUT THE AUTHORS

Stephen Long is a family forest owner who manages 95 acres of forestland in central Vermont. His journalism career began thirty years ago as a columnist for the *Santa Fe Reporter*. In 1994, he and Virginia Barlow founded *Vermont Woodlands* magazine, which became *Northern Woodlands* in 1999. In his 17 years at Northern Woodlands, he was the publisher and executive director in addition to his editorial work. He wrote hundreds of stories: editorials, features, and columns including Notes from the Puckerbrush and The Long View.

Virginia Barlow has been an editor and writer at *Northern Woodlands* since its beginnings in 1994. Her columns include the popular feature, A Look at the Season's Main Events. She has worked as a forester since 1990 when she earned a forestry degree from the University of Vermont, and she started Redstart Forestry, a forestry consulting company, a few years later.

Irwin Post is a forest engineer who lives in Chester, Vermont. He has managed woodlots in Vermont for over 30 years. His business activities have included consulting forestry, timber harvesting, sawmilling, woodworking, and harvesting white birch bark. He has written many articles for magazines, including *Northern Woodlands* and *Independent Sawmill and Woodlot Management*. His current research focuses on forest regeneration, especially in light of exotic and native invasive plants.

Michael Snyder is the commissioner of the Vermont Department of Forests, Parks, and Recreation. Prior to his appointment in January 2011, he served for 13 years as the Chittenden County forester. He is also a lecturer in forestry at the University of Vermont and writes the Woods Whys column for *Northern Woodlands*. Previously, he worked in forest ecosystem science at the Hubbard Brook Experimental Forest and in land surveying and forest management. He owns and manages a 91-acre forest in northern Vermont.

Charlie Thompson is a forester who has worked in the forest industry, as a consulting forester, and as a forestry educator. He is the former executive director of the New England Forestry Foundation and is the co-author of *Working with Your Woodland*. He owns woodlots in Vermont and Massachusetts.

Chuck Wooster was the associate editor of *Northern Woodlands* for 12 years. He owns and manages Sunrise Farm in central Vermont, producing vegetables, meat, and wood products from 300 acres. He is the author of two books on raising livestock, *Living with Sheep* and *Living with Pigs*, both published by Lyons Press.

Joe Smith, illustrator, has worked as a forester for 33 years and during that time has also pursued his love of drawing and painting, inspired by the New England landscape and the many beautiful and unique trees he has met. His illustrations have appeared in many local and regional forestry-related newsletters and magazines and he regularly shows his paintings through the Gardner Area League of Artists and other local artist organizations. He lives in Phillipston, Massachusetts.

ABOUT THE PUBLISHER

Northern Woodlands, formally known as the Center for Northern Woodlands Education, is a not-for-profit organization based in Corinth, Vermont. Founded in 1994, it seeks to advance a culture of forest stewardship in New England and New York by increasing public understanding of and appreciation for the natural wonders, economic productivity, and ecological integrity of the region's forests. Its chief educational vehicles are:

> *Northern Woodlands,* a quarterly magazine;
>
> *The Outside Story,* a weekly natural science column sponsored by the Wellborn Ecology Fund;
>
> *The Place You Call Home: A Guide to Caring for Your Land,* a series of geographically focused landowner guides;
>
> Two biweekly e-newsletters, one for general audiences and the other for educators.

In addition to *More Than a Woodlot: Getting the Most from Your Family Forest,* Northern Woodlands has also published *The Outside Story: Local Writers Explore the Nature of New Hampshire and Vermont,* a collection from the syndicated columns.

The organization's flagship is its magazine, *Northern Woodlands,* which reaches more than 14,000 readers predominately in the Northeast but also with subscribers in all fifty states and a dozen countries. *Northern Woodlands* has received awards from a broad spectrum of diverse stakeholders who care about the future of the region's forests.

For more information on Northern Woodlands and to subscribe to the magazine and e-newsletters, visit www.northernwoodlands.org.

Continue your journey with a subscription to *Northern Woodlands.*

Northern Woodlands magazine has been described as a perfect balance — it celebrates the natural wonders of the northern forest while recognizing the immense values the forest provides in supporting the local economy and culture of the Northeast.

Whether you've spent your lifetime in the woods or your interest has just been sparked, *Northern Woodlands* will strengthen your connection to the land with:

- skills to master
- ideas to ponder
- worlds to discover and rediscover

In *Northern Woodlands,* the woods and wildlife of New England and New York come alive.

Three easy ways to subscribe!

1. Visit us at northernwoodlands.org
2. Call us toll-free at 800.290.5232
3. Send your check to:
   Northern Woodlands, PO Box 471, Corinth, Vermont 05039

Annual subscription to our quarterly magazine is $21.50.

Northern Woodlands is a 501 (C) 3 tax-deductible educational not for profit organization.